Enduring
Dreams

ALSO BY JOHN MOSS

Patterns of Isolation 1974

The Ancestral Present: Sex and Violence in the Canadian Novel 1977

A Reader's Guide to the Canadian Novel 1981

Bellrock 1983

Invisible in the House of Mirrors 1984

A Reader's Guide to the Canadian Novel: Second Edition 1987

Arctic Landscape and the Metaphysics of Geography 1992

Editor

Here and Now 1978

Beginnings 1980

Modern Times 1982

Beginnings: Revised Edition 1984

Present Tense 1985

Future Indicative: Literary Theory and Canadian Literature 1987

From the Heart of the Heartland: Sinclair Ross, A Reappraisal 1992

Enduring Dreams

AN EXPLORATION OF ARCTIC LANDSCAPE

JOHN MOSS

Anansi

Published in 1994 by
House of Anansi Press Limited
1800 Steeles Avenue West
Concord, Ontario
L4K 2P3
(416) 445-3333

Canadian Cataloguing in Publication Data

Moss, John, 1940–
Enduring dreams: an exploration of Arctic landscape

ISBN 0-88784-549-5

1. Arctic regions.   I. Title.   II. Literary criticism

FC3956.M68 1994   971.9′03   C94-930062-4
F1090.5.M68 1994

Typesetting by Tony Gordon Ltd.

Printed and bound in Canada

*House of Anansi Press gratefully acknowledges the support of the
Canada Council, Ontario Ministry of Culture, Tourism, and
Recreation, Ontario Arts Council, and Ontario Publishing Centre in
the development of writing and publishing in Canada.*

For three extraordinary women: Virginia, my partner and friend, who fills the places in my life that words can't reach; Julia, my critic and mentor; and Laura, my indefatigable confidante. Also, for George Zarb and Fred Cutler, who have become inextricably part of the big adventure.

CONTENTS

Preface   ix

1   **A Place for Things to Happen:**
    Geography as Metafiction   *1*
2   **Waking the Dead**   *28*
3   **The Cartography of Dreams**   *53*
4   **On the Historiographics of Desire**   *90*
5   **Ultima Thule and the Metaphysics**
    of Arctic Landscape   *124*

Bibliography   *159*
Acknowledgements   *173*

PREFACE

*R*EMEMBER FRESH SNOW melting in your mouth when you were a child? That was what clean tasted like; the word and the sensation, inseparable. Now in July of 1993 as I bend to scoop a drink from the Sanguqiak — a whole river of meltwater — memory is transformed into landscape. The reflection of my face is obscured by the sloping shadow of my hat, so that what I seem is an absence, although I can clearly see the boulders and gravel of the river bottom within my projected shape. Five or six days from the nearest human being, in the backcountry of Baffin, I feel at home in the world.

The hat is a Stetson I picked up a couple of years ago in a little town just north of Laredo, driving through with Laura from Mexico. She bought one, too, but hers is still pristine while mine is old and battered. Julia worries about me alone on the tundra — although at least there's Jack (blue-black with limpid eyes, an obsessive retriever restrained at my camp by the bend in the river; an enforced day of rest after a hard week of trekking). In another week Virginia will travel from Lake Harbour up the Kuujuaq Valley, parallel to this one across the Meta Incognita, with news of Julia and Laura, George and Fred. We'll spend a month among the tributaries and ravines of Katannilik, and on the stone-strewn, windswept plateau that divides the two rivers.

Before leaving Bellrock I finished my Arctic book. During the last week under a heavy pack, negotiating my way through lichen disguised as rock and boulders pretending to be moss, with neither a camera nor a pen to make field notes, although I will remember this, I am caught between between loss and freedom — I am satiated, but with a huge and booming emptiness. This is the book I always intended to write, even before I had been to the Arctic. Over the past five years I've worked compulsively between detachment and passion; lived to write about what I was living, drawing from intellectual discourse and research, adventure and sport, contemplative evasions of language and thought; from many texts and a critical aptitude, from travel, teaching, and especially family, from imagination and a deep desire to know — and always with unusual sureness that this was what I should be doing. Closure is hard to imagine.

At first, out here on my own, I talked aloud against the quiet; after a day or two without reminders of a shared human presence, I drifted comfortably into silence, except for occasional encouragement to Jack and the odd expletive drowned in the green rush of water beside me or the sog of forming earth beneath my feet. Words and images slip perpendicular through the mind when each step among the rocks is a tactical manoeuvre and each gaze across the open tundra, strategy. Virginia is everywhere in this book, as she is while I walk. Of the many dimensions to my experience, the many levels and subtexts, some are a love story. It is Virginia's book as much as mine.

After stumbling earlier among some tiny succulents, I spent an hour trying to capture the elusive smell that kept me sprawled against the ground, long after the surprise of falling ebbed. And at night as I remember rivers surging through a sheer ravine I search for words to fix in mind the water's clarity, which on the roiling surface seems pellucid but drops in depths to crystal green. Sometimes in the evasions of words is a deeper kind of listening.

Sanguqiak, Kuujuaq, Katannilik — practise the Inuit names. They arise from the landscape itself. In time they seem familiar, the English names alien. Now and then I think of a writer like Wordsworth walking on weather-shorn grass in the brief meadows near the headwaters of these Baffin rivers, or of Whitman surmounting a pingo near Tuktoyaktuk to gaze inscrutably into the Beaufort Sea, of Lampman making tea from an iceberg, Atwood skinny-dipping with Kroetsch among seals. I have read many Arctic books and sometimes the Arctic is in everything I read.

Finding myself among words at the farthest reaches of comprehension, named in a language evolved as the expression of the landscape that has given it form and is uttered in every syllable — *pisukti*, the man who walks, *pisuktiuvunga;* and Virginia, for carrying her running shoes everywhere, training for future events on eskers, riverbanks, and terraced moraines, she is *oolati*, the woman who runs. Inuktitut fits uneasily into the Roman alphabet and Indo-European pronunciation. A word in Lake Harbour may be radically or subtly different in Pangnirtung or Iqaluit, just as the land itself may change. There is no correct spelling for words in a language like Inuktitut, alive in a place with the breathing of people; only restrictive approximations, delimiting voice by convention.

Today I find an articulate rectangle of stones on an exposed promontory; parallel to each long side, another row of stones. There would have been a wall-sided canvas tent here, set to catch the wind as an insect deterrent: against one rock, the chassis of a Matchbox toy; the black bakelite wheels still spin. The body, perhaps a double-decker London bus, is missing. I replace the chassis in the rock's shadow and think the thoughts of children. Back almost to my camp I discover an oval of stones tucked away in the shelter of a rock face and some huge boulders; six feet by nine, two metres by three, the stones nearly obscured in the deepening sediment. This was the base of an antler-raftered home when the language I live in was just beginning its present shape.

Jack is astonished to see me again. I have been gone ten hours and covered forty kilometres, if you can trust the map. After dinner I lie in my tent and write in the present tense — I have a pen, after all, the one I found where Virginia set it down in the lee of a rock a year ago when we came through on the Itijjagiac route from Iqaluit. I write of today on the map's back and, closing, search for the words of a stranger to convey where I am. Some errant lines of Yeats — it's better I don't know them exactly, easier to make them my own. My pleasure now, daylight briefly obscured in the Earth's shadow, is much as in that hour when the swan floats out upon the long last reach of glittering stream to give his final song, although it is only of the dying light I sing, to bring the dawn.

VIRGINIA LIGHTLY SKETCHING lines to be erased, filling blocks of colour in the spaces — she brought a book by Toni Onley with her up the Kuujuaq and reads assiduously at night his Arctic images, the washes, planes, and textures that represent his own austere and passionate experience. She's trying to capture what is there; he, what he sees. She, to comprehend the swelling imminence of Arctic landscape, and he, to reveal the artist's soul. Neither is possible, but the Arctic as a medium of desire is eloquent in its refusal to yield, generous in its capacity to complement their lovely follies — as my own.

1

A PLACE FOR THINGS TO HAPPEN:
GEOGRAPHY AS METAFICTION

*T*RYING TO DEFINE geography: the imposition of knowledge
on experience in a specified landscape. That's what I mean to say, but
it's so terse it seems evasive. Geography is essentially propriocentric;
it does not exist outside our awareness, but is entirely separable both
from us and our presence within it. The mind opens like an eye on the
landscape, and defines what it sees in terms of itself. The eye measures
light; distance and direction — geography articulates our solipsistic
vision of the world as knowable, as what we mean it to be.

Look north toward the sun. We have caught the turning world at rest.
Down the broad length of the Pangnirtung Pass light fibrillates in a
cloud of evanescent reds. The time is midnight and the sun, caught
briefly at nadir between the valley walls, begins to separate from
colour. Accompanied only by the hushed sounds of our breathing, it
breaks into a pale elliptical ascent and before long, for an hour or so
as it swings eastward, it will throw the glacial ridges of the pass into
deep shadow and leave us in full light, high on a western cliff, with the
day above, the night below. An inukshuk that marks our route back to
camp reaches from beneath us, up toward a crisp cerulean sky. We
know where we have come from, yet so illusory the darkening Earth
it seems hypothetical, a dream.

Time gathers around us, pressing through skin exposed to the cool
night air: celestial time, in the shifting sun; geological time, in the

contours of the land; paleocrystic time — not eras but aeons or ages — in the slowly moving surfaces of ice; generative time, in the distant muted colours of the grasses, the tumultuous profusion of remembered flowers, and the sibilant hush of wind against the landscape; human time, passages marked by inukshuit on the ridges below; time contained by the watches we wear to acknowledge duration; and the brief flicker of personal time, caught in the breath, in the randomness of private thoughts, in the chill of drying sweat and muscles heavy from the uphill climb.

Geography is a discipline, of course; and location — in a proscriptive sense, patterns determined by rule.

Geography is conditions, meant almost as metaphor. Arctic geography; conditions of climate, of will. To endure, be endured.

The struggle to define geography is a question of being. Where in the world are we? We yearn for a familiar perspective. We need geography, it seems. We invent it. Geography as history; and history, geography. Place marking time, and time in place.

It is early July 1991 and the midnight sun, lifting from the notch on the farthest horizon, will not fully set for a couple of weeks. We are six days north of the Arctic Circle on a rocky promontory above the Weasel River, Auyuittuq, south Baffin Island. We are outsiders here, backpacking; not the people of this land, not humans being but humans doing, our actions separate from our survival. Our experience in the pass is abstracted, shaped by chronometers and compasses. Geography is the instrument of our dissociation, when we fell from grace with the natural world.

We are wounded from the fall; we search the landscape for geography. We travel lightly, quickly, with excellent gear. We read maps and books; their lines articulate perception, anticipate terrain.

Traditional Inuit had no geographers. They were in the Arctic before it was north, before distance and direction fell into line; before north took hold and they became remote.

The word *remote* rings hollow, threatening.

It is April now and as the dull light fades I am of two minds, like a tree — as Wallace Stevens might have said — in which there are two blackbirds.

I am of two minds:
real in the landscape of the world,
remote in geography.

It has been like evening all day long; I am surrounded in my study, where I am writing, by souvenirs of Arctic adventure.

When Robert Falcon Scott perished in the Antarctic, the world was beyond his reach. He was remote. Read his dying journal; the poignancy is absolute: his British boyhood and British values were as real in this vainglorious predicament as if he had died at the foot of his own memorial statue off the Haymarket, not far from Buckingham Palace. His body, locked in repose beside his frozen cohorts, slowly swallowed by a continent of moving ice, swaddled in palliative woollens and a cracked canvas shroud, he remains a succinct and troubling symbol, although with time its meaning changes utterly.

And read the closing notes of Edgar Christian, written while he slowly starved to death in a cabin on the Thelon, Northwest Territories, spring 1927, in the company of two corpses — a young English officer, Harold Adlard, and his own beloved cousin, the renowned John Hornby, whose haunted dreams had led them there. In his last words before dying (not counting the words he might have spoken in necrotic delirium or as a wistful threnody to his dead companions), words written as a final letter home, the youthful Christian, not yet twenty, does not lament his miserable condition but pleads for parental understanding and forgiveness. His parents, in England, are immediate in mind, more real than death.

Through my study window at home in Bellrock, between Lake Ontario and the Canadian Shield, I watch the river, the brown cold water of the Depot Creek. I hear the murmuration of starlings through the glass (alien cousins of the raven, imported on the whim of a fanatic Shakespearean); I hear refracted cries of Canada geese heading to the Arctic and the summoning of solitary crows, the keening of a killdeer in the pasture across the river, and I listen with my heart for the ululation of loons. I watch for the great blue heron.

Soon the others will arrive: hummingbirds, robins, warblers, larks, and swallows, whippoorwills, sandpipers, red-winged blackbirds, bluebirds, and then the winter birds will appear again — they seem to hide in the trees in spring — the waxwings and the grosbeaks, the sparrows and chickadees and cardinals and jays.

I watch a beaver move through shadows against the far shore. It will circle our island, first with the current, then against it, scouting. Immune from trappers, beavers transform the landscape, drowning and devouring trees.

Standing high on a gravel esker above the Mackenzie Delta, the Arctic wind driving ice needles into my skin, I felt less remote than when peering through glass walls in the Cataraqui Town Centre. I once encountered my own footprints unexpectedly in dry mud, among the prints of a moose, a bear and her cub, walking birds, and what might have been a fox; suddenly I was as much a part of nature as the air. This was not on our island at Bellrock, where the shoreline marks the flooding of land two centuries ago to create a pond, a race, a flume, a drop, and power to mill the pines that once grew luxuriantly in the meagre soil here between landscape and geography, at the edge of north.

Landscape: the antithesis of geography.
Not landscape as in painting, where what you see is artifice, reality as art.
Not landscape as a verb, or as in gardening; with nature, a command performance.
Not landscape as a mental construct, the projection of human experience.
Nor as metaphor, the projection of human desire.

Landscape is the land, but is the sky, the weather, time. All there is, to be perceived, but does not include the perceiving; what may be known, but not the knowing. In which the mind may open, but not to open minds.

Landscape is the natural world without benefit of human consciousness, although not excluding human presence.
You may enter landscape, but in humility; if truly there, you cannot tell yourself apart from it.

When Virginia and I were on the Mackenzie in 1989, the Deh Cho as the Dene call it, paddling from Great Slave Lake to Tuktoyaktuk on the Beaufort Sea, 1,600 kilometres without a portage, we entered landscape gradually, bound by muscle fibre, sweat, and will to the river itself, to the great swift current and the scarred and scoured banks of sand, clay, gravel, rock, and runnelled muskeg. The Deh Cho was a living place for us, and we, alive within it. Sheer plod, the necessity to endure what we had set ourselves to do, slowly wiped away the predispositions of geography and history, maps and narratives.

Not all of them, but some.

We read Alexander Mackenzie's account of his journey to the Frozen Sea as we followed his route, camping when possible where he had camped, usually at the confluence of minor rivers and the overwhelming Deh Cho; sometimes guessing at the spots he pinpointed with Scottish rectitude because our instruments were less exact, our commitment to measurement less essential to our enterprise, and our strength not always equal to the vicissitudes of weather and current; sometimes inexplicably losing him on the churning, twisting line we pursued across the landscape and upon the charts he left us, and finding him again on the cusp of another landmark farther downstream, a day or two later.

(Explorer's field notes: it's hard not to get lost in words.)

Where geography is history, history is geography. We study geographers in school, the way other people study generals. So much for that — it's hard not to get lost in words.

This land the passionate must travel, must travel.
Douglas LePan said that, about Canada.

We studied him in school; a long poem called "Tuscan Villa." I learned from it the word *leviathan*. We didn't know he was Canadian. Recently I heard LePan on the CBC, on Gzowski. He's getting older, slower than I am. Virginia studied LePan. She won the high school graduation prize in geography: an Oxford atlas with a special insert on Canada.

LePan and Coleridge were in the same book with a royal blue cover: LePan writing about Italy, Coleridge about an Englishman's Antarctica. And someone else, an American. Whitman? Whitman found America through words; a great maker of maps, a poet writing America.

In Canada, mapmakers were passionate men; they made a place for things to happen. This is not without irony for the indigenous peoples they discovered. In the Arctic, mapmakers, especially those like Franklin, whose passions failed them, became myth. Or poems.

Beyond the Barren Lands, an ocean to the north, Vilhjalmur Stefansson made history with the Canadian Arctic Expedition, 1913–18, charting 100,000 square miles — proactive geography, for the sovereign state of Canada. This great illness, someone called it, snow-swallowed, a country of maps and dreams, circumscribed by survey lines. A land of ice and snow; brief summers, a winter land.

In December there is endless dark at noon in much of Canada; but six months later the diurnal sun extends to dawn. Clocks are meaningless in the soaring lightness of midnight: at Auyuittuq, poised on the western brink of the Pangnirtung Pass in the modulated white of summer night, we share a thermos of hot coffee and bannock fresh from evening dinner. There's not much talk. A few superlatives. The wind dies and everything, momentarily, is still.

Is silence, but for the intricate muted thunder sounds of a dozen waterfalls in melodious echoing along the valley walls.

We search the landscape for geography, to evade geography. To become part of the landscape.

Donne was wrong; we are each an island. Our only compensation, the possibility of archipelagoes.
Our only consolation, in this world we have made, the structures of geography.

Knud Rasmussen, on the Fifth Thule Expedition across the Arctic in the 1920s, discovered that Inuit could read maps without reference to north; could hold the landscape in their minds without respect to measured distance or direction, and reproduce its configuration to exact scale from their own experience in the world; not symbolism but the shapes of consciousness. I remember Julia very small would respond to photographs of people upside down before she learned to read right side up only. Before she learned the separate reality of photographs; to separate perception from perceived.

Year after year a great blue heron comes to Bellrock; always alone, he rides the air deliberately, settles across the river to watch for hours our pinioned swans gliding in unison within their island bay; he, from every vantage, solitary, a pterodactyl out of time, insufficiently evolved, and they, the royal mutes, bonded utterly, their soft reptilian necks affirming lineage as ancient as his own, although more obscured in symmetry.

This April there is only one swan to watch; the female is sitting out of sight on four blue eggs, each the size of a human heart, and the male swims in a furious rush, back and forth, watching the watcher, marking the line, the edge. The heron arrived this morning, stands motionless, then breaks free, rises awkwardly, and disappears.

We have named our swans but seldom use the names.

In the Arctic we saw whistlers; indigenous, like the heron, not the progeny of royal Europeans. As we emerged from the Mackenzie Delta, entering the Beaufort Sea not far from the abandoned settlement of Kittigazuit, we were attacked by Arctic terns and saw whistlers momentarily — the terns were enraged with territoriality; the swans, imperiously, disappeared against the morning light.

Roald Amundsen's statue in Tromsö, autumn 1990: stoic in stony repose, overlooks his sullen kinsmen, ignores admirers from Canada, drizzle, and the indignities of dissolving guano. Or was he bronze? My field notes say only that he is virtually an edifice, integral with the architecture around this small Norwegian square that opens along one side to the inevitable fiord, toward the sea, the swan's way, the whale's road.

From stone to bronze the wheel is run
Another course beneath the sun.
From bronze it turns at last to steel;
Another turning of the wheel.

From this point above the Arctic Circle, probably in the rain, Amundsen set sail aboard the tiny *Goa*, which now lies rotting in its cradle in Oslo harbour alongside the closed-in pavilions housing

Nansen's *Fram* and Heyerdahl's *Kon Tiki*. Amundsen fled the Arctic archipelagoes of Scandinavia, bound west beyond his creditors, past Greenland, to Canada. The Northwest Passage. From story into stone; soul, rendered from bone.

Thor Heyerdahl became a book, and Fridtjof Nansen a Norwegian statesman. Amundsen, who overshadows the indomitable Otto Sverdrup after whom a sizable portion of Canada is named, although few Canadians know it; Amundsen, who spun a log from the *Goa's* taffrail and etched a line in his wake across the top of North America; Amundsen, who beat Scott to the South Pole, although unsportingly he used dogs, ate them, and survived; Amundsen, his reputation both impaled upon that still point of the turning world where all directions measure north and drawn westward across the Arctic map; Amundsen had not the knack of dying an exemplary death, in a fusion of history and geography, nor of metamorphosis, living as story. He died in a plane crash in the Arctic, looking for someone else.

The immensity of it all; so cold spit rattles, words shatter.

The Arctic, reduced by geographic explication to ciphers, digits, points that occupy no space, lines with no dimension; words shatter, become facts.

Victor Frankenstein's monstrous parody of man strides among words across the ice floes into an oblivion not unlike eternity. There is a fine line between the two, oblivion and eternity.

Geographers with wry map parodies of the Earth imagine markers on the infinite, and measure distances among them to mark our place in the world, the condition of our soul.

Geography as metaphysics.
Arctic landscape and the metaphysical geographer — an extrapolation, much like Mary Shelley's Frankenstein, a parody.

Had Norway's greatest statue maker, Gustav Vigeland, made Amundsen's likeness in concrete, would immortality have been achieved — guano slowly leaching through the sculpted composite, displacing manufactured lime?

Sometimes irony is just the way it is.

No, I'm wrong. The *Goa* sailed from Christiania, renamed Oslo before her return, long after Amundsen was dead. It was Tromsö he flew out of, on his final flight, the one that in the minds of many never landed.

There is a large bronze bust of Amundsen in the Antarctica collection of the Canterbury Museum in Christchurch, New Zealand. It is by a sculptor named Vigeland, not Gustav, but Arne. The great carved nose gleams from the rubbings of passersby searching for luck. I waited until no one was looking, Virginia was wrapped up in the Scott artifacts, and rubbed Amundsen's nose.

Geography as metaphysics is plausible; for the geographer, appealing.

The beaver curled around a bullet, rolled, and sank. I look to the trees for justification, but there is only a soft wind, the quiet liquid echoes of water rippling against the island shore, and among the branches an intricate hush of small sounds. You can hear the bush dying as you fly north over the taiga, the muskeg, over tundra and across the Barrens to the polar sea, or journey by canoe or on foot over the sloping surface of the world into Arctic treelessness; and then there is silence. Then you can only dream the forgiveness of trees.

On the southern edge of Ellesmere, described by Aritha van Herk with touching clarity as an island like a woman on the verge of flesh, I lie uncomfortably on the gravel, trying to penetrate the purple intricacies of a gnarled clump of saxifrage no larger than my fist. I imagine being dead here, holding the posture of peering at wildflowers while my body desiccates in the northern desert air and freezes at summer's end to solid ice, or is torn apart by scavengers, or buried by the Mounties at Grise Fiord within the permafrost (so that I outlast this living generation to haunt my progeny when they dig me up [like they did poor Torrington on Beechey Island, 138 years after Franklin buried him, to look, do tests, and reinter, eyeballs glazed, still staring, his skin forever twenty, leathery as mine], or even if they leave me undisturbed).

Torrington, whose first name was also John, was chief stoker on either the *Terror* or the *Erebus*, and died while the Franklin Expedition was burying its dead; before they were scattered, half-eaten, across the landscape, macabre punctuation in the grim sentence pronounced upon the entire project. That's why he's still intact; because they buried him, and because the forensic anthropologist in charge of digging him out of the permafrost put him back again; Owen Beattie of Alberta, scientifically detached but human nonetheless.

Each tiny flower of saxifrage has five petals, each petal like a purple shield rising from a centre bed of orange rust, with stamen like dots of fire; short stalks rising from a mat of rusty green — from a foot away, pointillism as a natural phenomenon. From ten feet away, an impressionistic swatch of colour. From a hundred, pointillism again, a nervous dot among dots. Austere as gravel. From a thousand, a faintly purple hue on rumpled canvas, mixed with smoky greens of the sparse grasses and odd yellow flecks of Arctic poppy.

What would I have seen, had Seurat or had Monet, with his field of broken colours, never been? Had Gauguin or Van Gogh never painted flowers, painted light? Or Lawren Harris never travelled north? Saxifrage on Ellesmere comes in white, and creamy white with orange spots, as well as rusted purple. It is not much used for anything. Labrador tea (*Leduc Decembers*) is good to drink, some say, steeped in boiling water, although I have heard otherwise, as well. Of the evening primrose family, the broad-leaved willow herb (*latifolium*) is occasionally eaten, leaves and flowers both, by Inuit as salad. The flowers are mauve and darkly veined, the stems, the bluish-red of arteries, with leaves of livid green. Arctic cousin to the fireweed, it grows in enthu-siastic clumps near water.

The landscape is shaped in our perceptions by appetite, by imperatives and our desires; and shapes how we perceive.
Landscapes of the mind: worlds of sense and wonder. That is the title of a recent book by J. D. Porteous. That's a way of seeing things, I want to say. That's a way of seeing things.

Artists are the geographers of light. Colour, form, texture, edge, and imminence in a Lawren Harris painting of the Arctic — luminosity, the intimate austerity — place the viewer in perspective. How much we see through others' eyes; eyes of the dead.

We learn to read maps right side up, as geometric allegories of the outside world. But there are other ways of seeing maps, a play of lines and mass; and of seeing photographs, the play of shades on paper from a fixed position.

Monet's confession: he admired the light on a corpse while at vigil in the early dawn; he traced a threnody of light and colour on his dead wife's skin.
Monet was a photographer, shaping memory, making colours in the eye; and a metaphysical geographer.
Seurat never sold a painting. Van Gogh sold one. Lawren Harris was independently wealthy, a farm machinery fortune.
Matisse in his eighties drew the Arctic from photographic images.

Death in the human world is as deliberate and arbitrary as architecture; in nature, random, and utterly connected.

The Third International Conference of the Nordic Association for Canadian Studies, Oslo, August 9–12, 1990, was called "The Arctic: Canada and the Nordic Countries." A paper was given on Lucy Maud Montgomery. So much for that. Another was given on Margaret Atwood's *Surfacing*, whose characters, remember, drive north as far as

North Bay and then turn right then left and drive for a while in Quebec. This north is as close to the Tropic of Cancer, twenty-three and a half degrees above the Equator, as to the Arctic Circle, twenty-three degrees, twenty-nine minutes south of the North Pole. How could the meaning of Arctic so escape the Scandinavian sense of latitudinal rectitude, geophysical parallax?

Both papers were given by Canadians, Canadians who think the Arctic a direction, north a place (and perhaps it is).

Language is the problem.
Think of language sailing landscape, carried north. A language is not the same in different places; different languages do not exist in parallel. English and Inuktitut are alternate realities. What do dusk and dawn mean when skies are vaulting darkness through December and unending light in June? What does day mean when there is no dark, or night when there is no day? What does cold mean, where survival depends upon the solidity of winter; what does summer mean, mosquito-laden? Words skim on surface tension; language from elsewhere threatens to drown.

Only at the vernal or autumnal equinox do light and time in the temperate world and the Arctic coincide. There is equal light at the poles and at the Equator in every passage of the Earth about the sun, and equal darkness, but the year not the day is the measure. Meaning shifts among equations of light.

Snow in Kew Gardens, from a word imported by the Norse; snow in Gimli, where Manitoban Vikings pile it high beside the driveway; snow in the desert climate of northern Baffin, southern Ellesmere, skittering beneath the prefab houses at Pond Inlet or Grise Fiord, where memories of Greenlandic Norsemen are ancestral — how can you measure snow? How can you speak of snow in Tuktoyaktuk or Pangnirtung, where there are many snows and snow conditions, infinite textures, endless implications? Translation of the word *snow* from English into Inuktitut, *aput*, translated back to English means spread out. Unless you are measuring *perksertok*, snow drifting, or *massak*, snow mixed with water, or *ayak*, snow on clothes.

Snow: the colour of a dead man's skin. Said Brian Moore, echoing Monet. A dead white man, he might have said. Not the colour of an Inuk's skin. Snow, said Margaret Laurence. Honeycombed with black patches.

Language is the problem.
East or west are relative and, paradoxically, remain constant as you plod about the globe, perpendicular to the polar axis. North, however, alters with every move away from a given meridian, every move no matter how infinitesimal, from where you were.

Born on a shoulder of the Earth, this language thinks in four directions. East is east and west, west. There is a Far, but no farthest east, and a Far West, but no farthest. There is, however, absolute north, from which all directions measure south; and absolute south, where the Americans have built a geodesic research dome and are wary of strangers.

I haven't seen the great blue heron for several days. This afternoon, while thinking of beavers, I was distracted by the male swan, breasting the water in a furious rush to proclaim sovereignty on the moving river; and at times his great flapping wings, although pinioned, lifted him almost into the air. Within the folds of the female's wings I heard and caught glimpses of two cygnets. A third was dead and I removed it carefully; the fourth egg was rolled away from the nest.

Arctic: from the Greek for bear;
Nanuk, polar bear.
How many languages converge in every word?
If you listen, you can hear the clash of cultures in a twist of sound, in the silence of thought, the sound of thinking.

Nanisivik is geography in Inuktitut; the place where people find things. On a road bulldozed through the rough terrain between Arctic Bay and Nanisivik, on the north end of Baffin Island, each year a hundred runners from the south, and a few from the north, ascend, descend, traverse forty-two point something kilometres — I never remember the exact distance, but it's not from Marathon to Athens; it's from Windsor Castle to the gates of Buckingham Palace. A few runners run both ways, an ultramarathon: eighty-four point something kilometres. For distance runners, geography is unavoidable.

Marathon or ultramarathon, you run the midnight sun — so moving in the Arctic light, so exhilarating in the complexity of its achievement, of its mastery, so nearly perfect in the fusion of body, soul, and the world around that, having done it, you are changed, a runner always, with Arctic landscape in your mind, as much a part of you as breathing.

This year we have come, Virginia and I, with Laura, who ran the course in 1987 after high school graduation, and her friend Fred, with Julia and her fiancé, George, with my brother Richard, and Fred's mother, Fran. We have come to run the Arctic, where measurements of distance and duration merge in the endless subtle beauty of the Arctic sky and rough terrain, as they meet with every footfall along the gravel road across the Borden Peninsula, 720 kilometres above the Arctic Circle.

It is rare for geography, with such visceral eloquence, to proclaim itself irrelevant and landscape, everything.
Nanisivik is where people find things; themselves, the living world, natural religion.

Laura planted trees in northern Ontario, 3,000 on a good day, high-balling in muskeg bush to pay her way to Baffin, far beyond the tree line in another kind of north — where there have been no trees for light-years.

The first geographers were sailors with attitudes, and dreams.
Some went north, yearning for glimpses of Ultima Thule. Geography was to find their way home again.

Geography defines the Arctic relative to Greenwich; from Greenwich, everything is relative. The times of our birth and our demise, the locations, are measured from Greenwich. Distance and direction, mass and energy, the measurements of sound and light. Only in art is Greenwich not the absolute of everything.

Margaret Atwood, in the first of four Clarendon Lectures for 1991 delivered at Oxford University, spoke on image clusters of the north, as she calls them, in the Canadian imagination. Dress optional, the empress of ice cream reigned eloquence.

My dictionary of the moment says (attend to this):

> **north** [pronunciation symbolics] , *n*. 1. the direction to the left of a person facing the rising sun. 2. a cardinal point of the compass lying directly opposite south. 3. *(usually cap.)* a region or territory situated in this direction. **4. the North,** the northern area of the United States, lying to the north of the Ohio River and usually including Missouri and Maryland. — *adj*. 5. lying toward or situated in the north. 6. coming from the north. — *adv*. 7. toward or from the north. — north'ern [pronunciation symbolics], *adj*. — north'ern.most' [pronunciation symbolics], *adj*.

So much for that.
I suspect Atwood, the Canadian, of colonial revenge.
Americans write dictionaries.

She explains north to the Oxford audience, sharing her ability to adjust for deviation. The Arctic at Oxford: Robert Service. Sir John Franklin, an Englishman sailing the landscape, trekking through ice: a Canadian paradigm. Tom Thomson's quirky death by drowning in Algonquin Park; inevitable in a discussion of Canadian nordicity. Gwendolyn McEwen's Franklin, before she took up T. E. Lawrence, who also died in deeply troubled stages. E. J. Pratt. Mordecai Richler's Franklin episodes, ironies contextual. Word association, a northerly motif.

From Toronto everything Canadian is north; the Arctic, a semiotic
tragedy.

It is not by lack of ghosts we're haunted; vampires,
we preen before the absence of our own reflection.

We see ourselves in Thomson landscapes, on bank walls;
we see the Arctic through a drowned man's eyes
(it is as far from Algonquin Park to Ellesmere as to Paris).

Between metaphysics and the physical world,
we squander who we are.
When you measure reality from elsewhere, you are always on the
    edge.

The Arctic is shadowed, now, even at the summer and the winter
    solstice,
when there is either only light or the dazzling echo of its absence.
Geography has displaced the landscape;

misplaced it, perhaps,
as grown-ups misplace their childhood,
or a child, a mitt on an idiot string drawn up the sleeve.

Perception and notation are functions of experience; not being,
    itself.
You may situate yourself in landscape, within the landscape. You are
not in a privileged position;
you are landscape.

When outsiders first explored the Arctic, they were looking for
something else: wealth, a northwest passage, knowledge, glory. They
found violent conditions, contoured alien space. They failed to enter
the landscape. They wanted through it, or to endure it, or back out.
Of those who wintered over, many died. Others came, geographers;
searching for place, looking for limits — and in their random wake a

skein of patterns formed between the old worlds and the new, and as they named the landscape, measured it, marked it on maps, they brought it into line. Naming gave significance to their efforts, conferred meaning on the Arctic, made of barriers boundaries (rooted in fear), and of boundaries, barriers (rooted in ignorance). None had much interest in the Arctic itself. They were more concerned with north, how to make it relative and absolute. How to relate it to where they came from; how to get over it.

I want to talk of Frobisher here, the Elizabethan privateer who got lost in the Arctic on the way to Cathay and returned three times to scrape tons of pyritic rock from the landscape east of Iqaluit, eventually to deposit them near Greenwich.

I want to talk of Hudson, Davis, Munk; Parry and Ross, M'Clintock and M'Clure; of Kane, of Sverdrup; of Peary, Cook, and Steger; of Richard Weber; of polar tourism, the sometimes honest aims of science and adventure. But why? You can look them up, these geographers, make patterns of their lives, speak casually about them or with professorial authority. History answers: their lives are the convoluted syntax in which we struggle to read ourselves inevitable.

In a world with no centre, everything is marginal.

The town of Iqaluit on Koojesse Inlet near the head of Frobisher Bay was itself called Frobisher Bay through the American occupation from 1943 until 1963. Inuit names for places are descriptive; *qalunaaq* names (*qallunaat, qadlunah, kabloona, kablunait*, as whites are called for their bushy eyebrows) are expressions of sovereignty.

Is it possible to situate yourself,
except in landscape? If not, then we are lost;
victims of geography.
Think north.

My *Concise Oxford Dictionary of Current English*, published at the Clarendon Press, begins with the adverbial definition:

> **North**: Towards or in the region lying to the right of observer on equator at equinox who faces setting sun.

Interesting: the Americans, according to Random House, face the sun rising to ascertain north. The British face the setting sun. Canadians don't write dictionaries; we live a borrowed language.

For further definition, I turn to my massively compacted two-volume edition of the *OED*. I am told:

> **North**: (adverbial) Towards, or in the direction of, that part of the Earth or the heavens which (in the northern hemisphere) is most remote from the midday sun.

Remote, the word rolls like thunder through a midday sky. The sun. The sun, more or less overhead, or slipping off the horizon, or climbing up the morning's edge, determines north — if you are standing in the right place, at the right time, facing the right direction.

Such cosmology is Ptolemaic; pleasing in certain circles.
With no spin on the world, north and south are not polarities;
the solipsism of language and geography,
nothing more nor less than necessary.

I am exhausted by words. Somewhere along the Thelon I am camped, Virginia and I, drinking too-hot tea, talking about Hornby, who published nothing on his meandering years through the sub-Arctic, his lost life. We are near the river's junction with the Hanbury. Samuel Hearne was here on his journey to the Northern Ocean two centuries ago. And James Raffan, this summer, doing research. The light through the tent is the colour of autumn. This hasn't happened yet; but it will.

Hornby's silence draws us to this confluence of time and rivers, this place, familiar and strange. It is not far from where, with Captain James Critchell-Bullock, a twenty-three-year-old Englishman, Hornby wintered in 1925 in a cavern dug from a sandy esker, a hole in the Barren Grounds covered with skins and dirt. Roughly two years later, in a low cabin not far downriver, at age fifty, he was dead of starvation, the victim of his own consuming need to endure extremes, dead with two companions, the one his young cousin Edgar Christian, who wrote home before he died and outlived Hornby by a month, surviving on offal, skins, and bones, and prepared himself for death in early June, wearing a heavy grey sweater over a khaki shirt, grey flannel trousers cinched with a silk handkerchief, a muffler loose around his neck, winter moccasins with puttees (according to George Whalley's book), and two red Hudson's Bay blankets pulled over his head. When Christian was found, his desiccated skin, the colour and texture of the Barrens in summer, taut against his face, he seemed ageless and was taken for Hornby, whom he had wrapped in a crude shroud, as he had the corpse of Harold Adlard.

Time breaks at the confluence of rivers, among the contours of surrounding landscape. History and geography enter each other; memory and perception merge.

Listen. We listen to an evening breeze from the northwest, playing the water beside us in whispers, sliding among the low shrubs and rogue grasses, shadowing with sound the tussocks and earth, echoing the pattern of gnarled sticks impressed against the sky. We can almost hear Raffan and his party, camped here while he makes notes for a dissertation on comparative responses to landscape. And we can hear Hearne, camped generations earlier with Matonabbee, on their way to the Coppermine River and the massacre of "Esquimaux" at Bloody Falls that would become infamous after Hearne's account was published in 1795, although it may not ever have happened.

Listen, we can hear ourselves breathe. Here, by the Thelon, we can almost hear John Hornby think. Not words. Tortured elements; the searing pleasures of water, land, sky. Water pretending to be land, to be sky, to be water. He, beyond all, refused the linear, the sentence, the map. He entered the landscape, but never forgot where he came from — and that killed him. He never became the landscape he entered, and that killed others.

The sky in the evening at this time of year is tangerine, and in the morning it is lemon; and as the sun dips into the horizon, our tent turns from translucence to marble, to suede, to coolness the texture of silk, and in the morning after the briefest of nights it is lemon, the colour of a drowned man's skin.

We haven't been here yet. I imagine this, in May, in my study at Bellrock, on the Shield's edge, near the meeting of Depot Creek and the Napanee River. Time breaks, like the surface of an infinite pool; a landscape unshaped by the instruments of our fall from grace.

Time, a landscape without geography, like books at random on my study shelves, like north.

Bracebridge is two hours north of Toronto. We often speak this way: north qua north, location in terms of time, acknowledging a specific cultural context in which distance and direction intersect in a statement of duration; the geography of getting there.

And the geography of nowhere: Hartwell's is a drinking spot in Ottawa, named, if the plane crash fragments mounted in the foyer are to be reckoned with, after Martin Hartwell, the downed flier in the Territories who cannibalized his dead companion, a nurse, and survived. There is a pattern here: of all that could be said, nothing is enough.

From Daphne Marlatt's *Ana Historic:*

> the silence of trees
> the silence of women
>
> if they could speak
> an unconditioned language
> what would they say?

A 28 p stamp: Greenwich [1884 — MERIDIAN — 1984]: a red line slashes the stamp like a meticulous cancellation mark, cuts through the dead centre, following precisely the roof line of what must be a very important building set among trees.

An Inuk, fishing, lies across the ice,
the shadow of her parka filling perfectly
the circle of broken water,
waiting for a fish to come.

At home she
watches wrestling and the weather
and dreams of a fish
rising through the air
like a ballad.

My *Oxford* dictionary, the large one, falls open at **Arctic**. This is a truth too trite to invent: the page is marked by a loose photograph, an eight-by-ten glossy, of Mazo de la Roche standing four inches high on a huge mass of gnarled ice, accumulated frozen surf of Lake Ontario, I think, or Lake Erie. She stares wistfully northward, into the camera's eye. The sun is on her right. Her posture is romantic; her stillness subtly dramatic. She is wearing a short mink jacket and a white fox muffler; the head hangs listlessly at her waist, with the tail incongruously protruding from just below her left ear. Mazo is too young to have written *Jalna* yet. The ice looks like refrozen vanilla ice cream. The picture was given to me by her cousin and lover, Caroline

Clement of Rosedale, and has marked the *Oxford* Arctic for a good thirty years, evading time, although I put it there originally, I think, to flatten it or keep it clean.

Under **Arctic** as an adjective, metaphysics merges with astronomy, geography is reduced to affirmation or consent: the *Oxford* quotes from the *Penny Cyclopaedia of the Society for the Diffusion of Useful Knowledge*, 1834 edition, volume 2, page 289:

> Every different latitude had a different arctic circle; and in the latitude in which astronomy was first cultivated, the great bear just swept the sea, and did not set, whence the boundary circle obtained its name.

The Arctic as geography was cultivated in a place where horizons circumscribe the celestial and boundaries are projections of being.

Another beaver: it keeps to the shadows of the far shore, eyeing my trees from across the water. The tree line is the beginning of south; treelessness, an absence only from elsewhere.

The beaver, a rodent leviathan, emblem of a northern nation for the value of its flayed, flenched, and desiccated skin; its shining fur.

In 1990 we sailed from Hammerfest to Kirkenes on the Barents Sea aboard the Hurtigruten *Nordnorge*, one of a dozen sea-road vessels threading the fiords of Norway from the North Sea to Europe's Arctic, pleating Norway's coast into a sublime communal garden shaped by history, myth, and political desire. As our tiny Citroën was hoisted on a sling to the fo'c'sle deck, as we settled into our panelled cabin, dined sumptuously and drank fine wine, as we slept and woke, breakfasted, relaxed in the cool morning breeze, and disembarked at Kirkenes, a stone's throw from the Soviet Union, thoughts of Nansen, Amundsen, and Sverdrup drifted through my mind.

What must their dreams have been, to follow ancestors who had sailed from the settled shores of Scandinavia for regions, as Nansen envisioned them, wrapped in the profound sleep of death? God knows, they explored magnificently, the landscape, adventured with deliberation, celebrated their achievements in writing of heroic modesty. And their genetic countrymen, Rasmussen, Stefansson, and Freuchen, explored its human side; captured the landscape and its people in books. What preparation, the fiords and archipelagoes of Europe, their study of atlases and navigation, eugenics and geography, their love of country and uncommon enterprise?

We drove from Kirkenes to Amsterdam in a week on good roads all the way, except through Sami sections in the north of Finland where they were as rough, at times, as the Dempster Highway or the graded gravel road to Yellowknife.

I make notes in April, notes in May, souvenirs of contemplation and desire. I dream the Arctic in summer, I dream sensual contours, the memories of ice and stone, skies of lapis lazuli, soft folds of light and broken fields of muted colour, alive with the innumerable murmuring of insects. I dream myself in the Arctic dreaming. And make notes, and think.

Think of the beauty of receding terrain,
yourself, a runner,
running hills at Nanisivik.
Think of hills —
folding into shadow, breasting light,
each imagined bank of hills more faded,
softer, sensual in the distance,
until in the far distance the final bank
has almost the opacity of sky.

This vista of the earth in waves,
successive and receding planes of diminishing intensity,

is in the countryside tradition of Cezanne;
but hills don't fade,
especially if you're running them.

With every footfall the Arctic
rises to embrace you;
pellucid air displays the landscape
like a Chinese painting —
the primacy of perspective, vestigial,
you, the runner, are
inseparable from what you see.

Julia and Laura will be home soon with George and Fred. The six of
us will plan our next trip north. Soon Virginia and I will travel the
Thelon, looking for the subtext of Hornby's silence, his story. And
after that, again the High Arctic. Ellesmere, perhaps. We're drawn to
islands. To Arctic light, the Arctic air.

I was once in a room in Havana, a high-ceilinged and smoky room,
with some Canadian writers and a cluster of Cubans, delegated to meet
us on behalf of the state. In this smoky tropical room a handful of
distinguished Canadian writers, accustomed to explaining north to
Canadians and Canada abroad, were entertained as honoured guests
and Canada never came up. Culturally neutral, we left no impression
at all.

I stand beside my grieving swan; do not tell me swans don't grieve.
Yesterday the male raged at all intrusion. Today, while his mate preens
her soiled down, having misplaced the bodies of her dead cygnets
against the ground, he stands in awkward pride and shares with me his
solitude in confraternity. I know this. It is my responsibility. These
swans are named and, pinioned, incapable of flight. The great blue
heron is nowhere to be seen.

I saw mute swans in Havana; and whistling swans on the Mackenzie
Delta, although when Virginia photographed them they flew against

the light and left on the print only a blur of moving white, a concentration of the sky.

It is easier at home
to write Canada down,
and abroad, to leave it there.

Our oldest oak was felled last fall. It was the only ancient oak left on
the island, growing long before the sawmill when the river was lower
and the island not yet islanded.

Time is a river only by convention; chronometers of stone, of ice, of
genes and generation, mark every passing moment, infinite. And as
you move through Arctic landscape, if you are a runner running,
memory and anticipation merge with every falling step; sky and earth
become each other, and you inseparable from what you see.

In these words, set now in this way of passing, there is no centre; there
are no margins; no borders. This is not a geography of the imagination,
or of the soul or mind. It is an essay of words; essay as landscape.
Fiction; as all writing is, it is fiction. Some things have not happened,
after all. A poem; not exactly. How passionately we miss the world.

Plan for an Arctic book (plans for myself):

each section in a different mode; diverse facets and a Möbius loop of
endless contemplation, intimations of destruction, of renewal. Archipelagoes in a text without limit. Landscape, and no horizons.

The Arctic air is filled with light,
 — it is important to know this —
not diurnal day, the sun quotidian,
but seasonal, trembling azure,
in winter shimmering silk,
against the sempiternal night.

The Inuit were north
of nowhere,
on the boundary of nothing,
until they were discovered there.
The ironies are absolute. I write this
as an outsider, native only to geography;
a visitor, for a while less remote.

Arctic landscape
enfolds the consciousness
in light.
The light is spatial, seasonal,
the light is air and ice and stone,
not the measure of our daily spin between polarities
(rolling clockwise, east from west
as we pursue our way about the sun).

We isolate ourselves
on the surface of a sphere;
locate ourselves with mathematical
exactitude, the metaphysics of geography.
But maps are not the same as memories;
the erotics of space
are now, at best, a dream.

Walk carefully through Arctic landscape;
one footprint in the tundra could last a hundred years;
on spring ice, eternity.

2

WAKING THE DEAD

I AM WRITING this in Mexico on the shore of Lake Chapala. The flowers here are foreign, even the ones I'm familiar with. Poinsettias are the size of trees. The weather never changes; opaque air that drifts south from Guadalajara is lifted by the burning hills around the lake to become an iridescent blue. Sunlight scours tumultuous landscape in the distance, and sun-drawn shadows etch gullies on the closer hills, like vein marks on the underside of desiccated leather. Mimosa and spirea grow wild against adobe ruins above La Canacinta, and near the receding waters of the lake the garden flowers loom so high that you can see them shadowing the houses, behind walls, as you walk the narrow roadways to Ajijic, or as you run along the dry mud flats, looking north. I am thinking of the Arctic.

Writing is a most unnatural act; literary criticism, unspeakable, an evasion of chaos and the singularity of death. (Yet writing now is second nature and reading how we entertain the world.) Jorge De Cuchilleros: *The Invention of Time*, 1984.

The Arctic of outsiders is a landscape of the mind, shaped more in the imagination by reading than by experience and perception. (For those who read, the dichotomy between knowledge and experience invariably resolves in favour of knowledge. Nothing do we find so real as written words.) For those who have never been to the Arctic, this is the only northern reality they know, this world gleaned in fragments from narrative accounts by explorers and adventurers, scientists and artists; by all who endeavoured to capture in words those awesome ineffable spaces and planes in which they are alien, and often of which they are more than a little afraid.

Words in narrative deliver images deep within, where the visceral encoding of seen and unseen merge, and the artfully imagined takes precedence over actuality. Such is the power of art to organize the mind. Narrative landscape passes from imagination into memory. Through language we come to know what we have never known, with no means to challenge authenticity but through rules of rhetoric and artifice, inappropriate measures in a world beyond the text.

The imagined Arctic draws from a variety of sources. It may be enhanced by the primal beauty of photographs by Fred Bruemmer or Mike Beedell, by the paintings of Lawren Harris or Toni Onley, A. Y. Jackson or Doris McCarthy (all of which convey the Arctic landscape as a genre with distinct conventions of its own); it may be shaded in the reader's mind by the theatrical backdrops of Robert Flaherty's silent film *Nanook of the North*, or coloured by iconic scenes from the National Film Board or the sublime wilderness of *The White Dawn*, a film made from the novel by James Houston. But for the most part the landscape of the imagined Arctic is a written world, words devoted inevitably to the articulation of alien imperatives and dreams.

Walking from La Canacinta, where we live in a garden of colours, into Ajijic along the beach, running from Ajijic to Chapala and back, between dry mountains and water, I search the faces of the people. This is an expatriate enclave rather than a tourist haven; most outsiders own their flowered garrisons, or rent them by the season, and look comfortably at home. The native Mexicans command more interest, their ancient lineage on this continent sometimes barely evident; often so distinct that Spanish seems inappropriate as you mutter suitable greetings for the time of day. Occasionally they smile at your discomfiture. Embarrassed, you think of movie Mexicans, and find yourself in borrowed terrain, remote.

For people native to a place, landscape is an extension of being, as intimate and far-reaching as genealogy, an existential fact. If the Arctic imagined by outsiders encroaches on Inuit perceptions of their own world, they will see themselves as separate from the land, and the landscape, increasingly unreal.

Driving to Guanajuato with Virginia and Julia, I am thinking of the Arctic. We read about Guanajuato in the guidebooks, how the heads of Father Hidalgo, of Allende, Aldama, and Jiminez were impaled at the four corners of the granary in 1811 and left there for a decade; we are haunted by the prospect of row upon row of desiccated human bodies on public display at the Museo de la Momias; we listen to a tape of Billy Joel singing over and over again "It's My Life."

We read from three complementary books and locate ourselves on a variety of maps. I am thinking of words, the Arctic as words. I listen from behind the wheel to Billy Joel, to Julia and Virginia, who take turns reading aloud the story of Mexico. The dry hills unfold as we move toward them, and flutter past like pages.

At Guanajuato's edge the road dips underground and follows the course of ancient sewers into the heart of the city, where ramps lead up to a garden square draped in bougainvillea and the shadows of trees. There are posters for Cervantes everywhere. It is difficult to know whose world this is: in the peoples' faces you can see their history as a sequence of displacements. I remember the short story by Audrey Thomas about the mummies of Guanajuato and an abortion and the problems of language. When I try to describe it to Virginia and Julia it seems more like a literary exercise than a haunting piece of fiction.

Buenas tardes, señor.
¿Habla usted inglés?
¿Cómo se llama en español?
Gracias.

It might seem of only passing interest that Mary Shelley contains the tale of Victor Frankenstein and his monstrous creation within a frame story set amid the ice floes of the High Arctic, or that Jules Verne's intrepid adventurers under Captain Hatteras plant the British flag and enjoy a cup of coffee on a volcanic island at the North Pole in 1861. It is more worrisome when Farley Mowat amends Samuel Hearne's journal of his journeys across the Barrens to make the original narrative more "authentic," or when he alters the lay of the land to make a first-person account of northern people more compelling or dramatic; or the details of animal behaviour, to make himself seem more humane.

Government policies on the north are made in consequence of how outsiders imagine it to be. Legislation affecting land claims, ecology, and human welfare is enacted on the basis of an Arctic written into the imaginations of legislators whose own experience of the north is often limited to, and always shaped by, what others write of it. Farley Mowat's writings shoulder a burden they were never meant to bear. At best he has engendered a widespread public interest in the Arctic. At worst he makes created facts seem true; his truths, the essence, for southerners, of northern actuality.

Unlike Arctic fiction writers such as Houston or Yves Thériault who strive for authenticity as a literary effect, unlike Verne or R. M. Ballantyne or Richard Rohmer whose ironic use of verisimilitude is meant to heighten drama in their romantic fantasies, Mowat undertakes to speak for the land itself and for its people. He writes as advocate, spokesman for a landscape in which, by birth and sensibility, he is an outsider. Yet it is through the work of Mowat and of others over centuries whose narratives have simulated Arctic actuality that the imagined Arctic has taken shape and inappropriate sovereignty been imposed.

Words separate us all from paradise, and bind us to it. From the splendours of chaos, through knowledge and death, they have led us to dream; and written, have given us history, given us time. Fear of the absence of time, of silence and the comforts of chaos; this is the legacy of language committed to print, words separated from consciousness and the traditions of speech.

And what is the cadence of silence? In Guanajuato the deceased whose rental dues have lapsed for half a decade are disinterred, the ordinary dead, discarded; but some, whose sand-seared bodies retain unusual qualities of interest, are laid in row upon row of glassed-in shelves for the curious to contemplate, to venerate, revile; arranged like sentences in the syntax of death, their postures, articulate.

Within the garden walls at La Canacinta, in the house where I am working, exploring the meridians and parallels of language in pursuit of northwest passages that never were but in the dreams of writers writing out their lives on linen parchment or on cheap acidic paper, where I can see above the mist of Lake Chapala to the leathery hills, dry mountains running the central Mexican plateau, where I am surrounded by flowers in garish profusion and stunted fruit trees coiled against the sun, where my family take turns visiting from Canada while I write, read, and watch American TV on satellite, where I relax after running for hours on the ragged beach, I am dreaming in a language of which I only grasp the roughest edges, edges that break off in fragments when I touch them.

Buenos días, señor.
¿Cómo está?
¿Cómo se llama en inglés?
Bueno, gracias.

Words, spoken, breathe; written, preserve only the remains of life. With every text a narrative (through structures of grammar, the fixity of ink, if nothing else), each, affirming order, denies the necessary chaos of human consciousness. Written words speak silence; souvenirs, like photographs, of having been. Phonetics, unspoken, have the stillness of death. And now we have discovered pictorial equivalents of writing, chemical and electronic hieroglyphs. We have nearly perfected the mummification of being: photography, like writing, freezes narrative (a convention of shadows and light); television, with its illusions of movement, is a parody of text, itself a parody of life, like movies and theatrical displays. We have learned to read our lives, to watch and even live our lives, in retrospect.

If Mowat's writing seems to many in the north inadvertently imperialist, consider the Arctic writings of people whose function was to advise southern bureaucracies for purposes of policy and entitlement. Reports to the British Admiralty, to the Hudson's Bay Company, to the Canadian government, to the National Geographic Society, contain strong elements of narrative, of story. All else is data. And story inevitably distorts. Story is shaped by the desires of the narrator; what is it he wants, and why? It is shaped by the imperatives that led him to write; what do they want, those who empowered him to be there and to write about it? What do the conventions of narrative demand? What do his readers expect?

And if the reports of such men (invariably until the last few decades writers of the Arctic were male) were transformed into works for public consumption, distortions were compounded . The Arctic landscape in published narratives by Samuel Hearne in the eighteenth century, for example, by Charles Tuttle in the nineteenth, or Vilhjalmur Stefansson in the twentieth, was subject to contrivance and invention, every bit as much as the Arctic in *Frankenstein* or Verne's *The Desert of Ice*, or anything of Farley Mowat. Yet Hearne wrote his original account as a matter of record for the Hudson's Bay Company, and Tuttle and Stefansson, for the government of Canada (although Stefansson served a variety of masters, with a variety of motives, including the necessity to generate capital for future efforts).

D. H. Lawrence wrote *The Plumed Serpent* on the shores of Lake Chapala; "Quetzalcoatl," he called it then, named after the Toltec demigod anticipated by the Aztecs in a Second Coming, under whose dispensation Cortez came — slouching, perhaps, toward the golden city, broaching paradise. He took ten weeks to write it. By all accounts he was unhappy in Mexico. Most of Malcolm Lowry's Mexican binge, *Under the Volcano*, was written in Canada — where he, too, was unhappy. Mexico, on the Day of the Dead, was a place for dying, and Canada, a place for writing death down. It is the mark of genius and of despair that each man's fiction is both epitaph and memoir.

Personality is an emanation of the text in all but the very best. So Virginia Woolf said of Shakespeare and of Jane Austen and about no one else, except perhaps herself, by implication. For the rest, words speak themselves and re-create the world in their writer's image. Words issue parallel realities — which we take to be more real in writing than the unreality we live. And life becomes a metaphor.

Distortions of the Arctic landscape are even more likely in accounts of personal exploits, such as the polar adventures of Robert Peary and Will Steger, than in the writing of anthropological explorers like Stefansson or Knud Rasmussen. Anyone who features himself in his own narrative, whether explicitly like Mowat or Peary, or surreptitiously like Stefansson, inevitably documents the landscape and its people as extensions of his own experience.

We expect this fusion of intention and surroundings in works that openly subsume the Arctic into literary constructs. The haunting confessional meditations of J. Michael Yates at Great Bear Lake, the witty and evocative metafictions of Aritha van Herk on Ellesmere, the confabulations of Robert Kroetsch in "How I Joined the Seal Herd," F. R. Scott's poetry about a quick trip down the Mackenzie with Pierre Trudeau, the Arctic poems of Al Purdy, of Jim Green, of Paulette Jiles, all such works openly declare the Arctic landscape as subject, not object. They are no more to be held accountable for authenticity than is the effervescent doggerel of Robert Service or are Jack London's irrepressibly inventive yarns of northern peril.

(In *The Great Bear Lake Meditations*, what J. Michael Yates has to say is pleasing and may be true, but it tells more about him and about being human than about the world it seems to describe:

On this island too north for trees, I fish for arctic char. The ice-blue landscape is the colour of the ice-blue water. A small seal reclines and watches from a rock across the stream. I lie that only water passes between the seal and me.

This expression of contemporary angst is in the literary mode of an Anglo-American tradition quite alien to the north [yet ironically appropriate].

Al Purdy creates a haunting evocation of Baffin landscape in his Arctic sequence *North of Summer*, yet the essence of the following image is metaphysical, not physical — it asks not where is here, but what am I?

> Brief Arctic twilight
>   darkens the stone island
> something neither day nor night begins
> blue water loses what makes it alive
> shadows aren't shadows but proxy things
>   that represent things
> and I wonder what I represent

And so it goes. Each literary writer, informed by convention and the demands of personality, transforms the Arctic landscape into a literary device.)

When Fred and Laura arrive at La Canacinta a week before Christmas, we have dinner in Ajijic and immediately plan a trip to Mexico City, via Guanajuato. Virginia and Julia and I have never talked about the mummies. The Museo de la Momias shocked us into a conspiracy of parallel and haunting silences. But the town is very beautiful and I want Laura to see it. Back home in Bellrock we will speak of this, how each of us carried identical unspoken images away from that terrible place, in that beautiful town. We spend several hours in Guanajuato this time, exploring the labyrinthine walkways carved among the multileveled hillside houses, and we have lunch in one of the shaded restaurants on the Jardin de la Union.

When I was very young, my father drove me to the Royal Ontario Museum and left me there for the afternoon. The glass-encased tableaux of Indians and wild animals were unconvincing, less real than Eaton's Christmas window mannequins or my grandmother's fox fur collar with the glass eyes. But when I wandered into the Egyptian wing and found the open sarcophagi, I was immediately enthralled. I lingered with my face against the cool of the glass of one in particular, transfixed by the orange hair pressed patchily against a leathery skull. It was not terror I felt but empathy. These were the remnants of a person there, and only time — for the first time realized as something palpable, implacable, taunting — stood between our discourse, for it didn't occur to me that she wouldn't speak English.

Thinking of the Arctic in La Canacinta, about time and the reality of words, about written language, how it has misplaced the world, I also think about the acrid thickness of the air in Mexico City, flatulent buses and trucks on the streets of Guadalajara, the fetid dinginess of village side streets, mimosa, and cactus among the Aztec ruins at Teotihuacan, ruins built upon the ruins of a civilization contemporary with Imperial Rome; I think about ancient Egypt, Ozymandias, the Shelleys and Byron in Italy, Frankenstein. About the Arctic. I think and read about Mexico and gradually Mexico becomes a part of all that I have read. I assimilate the patterns of recorded syntax more readily than my own discordant memories. Sequence, connectedness, notions of temporality derive from text: inchoate senses are obtrusive; maps replace dreams; books, memories; history, tradition; and geography, the landscape.

My computer is set up so that I can simultaneously see what I am thinking and the hills across the lake; from the screen I look beyond the flowered wall, beneath an unchanging azure sky, to the burnt hills like mouldering leather draped across a pile of bones, hills moving in the torpid air like starving animals — yet not unlike the desert hills of northern Baffin; and in my writing sometimes I dream straight lines of light that fall on the ragged earth from kaleidoscopic fissures overhead, and sometimes I remember clouds as they collapse against the wheeling Arctic sun.

(It is usually a simple matter to identify invention in a literary work, and convention, as well, although you may be unfamiliar with the antecedents. In these lines by F. R. Scott, the Arctic landscape draws heavily on precedent, even though the idea, while dismaying, is inspired:

> In land so bleak and bare
> a single plume of smoke
> is a scroll of history.

As in the examples from Purdy and Yates, a narrative voice intrudes to declare the primacy of human presence over landscape, effect over authenticity.)

In poetry or fiction there is seldom ambiguity about what is intended as "realism," capable of evoking in the reader's mind a scene appropriate to the narrative, and the "realistic" — a scene invoking something in the reader's memory, something already known. The reader can only take so much of the latter, without the narrative being undermined in imagination.

We no more want James Houston, for all his knowledge and empathy, to re-create the actual Arctic in his novels than we would expect Thomas Hardy to render England's West Country as a historical document, or William Faulkner, the American South as a social treatise. As artists, these writers (like Margaret Laurence with Manawaka, Matt Cohen with rural Ontario, David Adams Richards with the Miramichi, Jack Hodgins with Vancouver Island) transform place into literature, landscape into literary experience.

But what about writers of rhetoric? Writers such as Barry Lopez in *Arctic Dreams* or Rudy Wiebe in *Playing Dead*? They write beautifully, filling page after page with evocative descriptions of landscape mingled with musings and meditations — and, in the case of Lopez, scientific reportage. What of Hugh Brody, whose *Living Arctic* is for many outsiders a breakthrough in coming to know the far north as a world parallel to but unlike their own? Are these writers so different from Hearne or Stefansson? The effectiveness of what they write similarly depends upon our taking them at face value, as purveyors of the literal truth.

What about writers of personal adventure, who feature themselves at the narrative centre? Writers such as James Raffan in *Summer North of Sixty* or M. T. Kelly writing about a canoe trip in *Saturday Night* or Richard Weber and his three Canadian cohorts writing about the Canada-Soviet transpolar expedition in *Polar Bridge*? If we doubt the authenticity of the landscape, or the icescape, against which their dreams unravel, their achievements, no matter how thoughtfully described, seem empty.

Much of the controversy surrounding Peary eighty-some years after he apparently reached the North Pole comes of the fact that in the narrative of his achievement he ran out of landscape (as well as credible witnesses). His ghostwriter, A. E. Thomas, pleaded in the name of literary plausibility for more details than his notes provided. Mackenzie, pedestrian in prose style and narrative sense, at least offers the exact measurements and bearings upon which to rest his claims of exploration. The land exists beyond his text. And Franklin, for all his limitations, has never seriously been doubted for having covered actual terrain.

Written narrative is arrested motion: words fixed in syntactical design promise endless renewal. There is no limit to meaning on the airless page.

When at first there were texts, then every text was sacred, and to live forever became necessity, at least for those familiar with the tricks of transcending time through characters and runes. Words connected worlds; the body, even dead, became the symbol of another realm of being. The typologic fusion of language and belief displaced collective memory and natural religion; landscape, bound by narrative and meaning, became mere imagery in the service of progress and of immortality.

A single most enduring image of the Arctic is the literal face of death; three faces, merging as a frozen composite. There is the close-up photograph of John Torrington, chief stoker on the Franklin expedition whose thawed body had been sealed in the permafrost on Beechey Island for 138 years; and there is the mummified Greenland baby whose empty eye sockets stare out at the camera like the limpid eyes of a seal pup caught just before slaughter; and there is resignation, bewilderment, and defiance in the studio portrait of an Inuk child, Minik, posed in native costume, 1897, in New York City. (Minik "boarded" with his father and several other Inuit in the basement of the American Museum of Natural History; after his father died, his bones were cleaned and moved upstairs to be, as the New York *World* wrote it, given for his coffin "a showcase, his shroud a piece of plate glass.") Studio lights put a flat gleam in Minik's eyes. Torrington's are milky; his lips drawn tight against his teeth. The Greenland baby, buried alive with its mother (according to the *National Geographic*), is on display in Nuuk. Torrington has been reinterred beneath the frost line. Minik was given a Christian burial; his father's bones remain on file.

Even when the documentary writer makes no pretense at being objective, he still relies on the authority of the text to ground conviction in reality, the personal in landscape.

(M. T. Kelly, describing a canoe trip into the Thelon area, seems to confuse himself with his subject in a surge of sentimentality: "Nature may well be a 'maniac,' and I couldn't delude myself this place cared for humans. But for a moment, against all reason, as the water shivered and the light flew, I knew the land was capable of love." James Raffan, in *Summer North of Sixty: By Paddle and Portage Across the Barren Lands*, quite deliberately, and with lyrical restraint, suggests something similar about the landscape as a projection of personal desire. Sitting on a hill, high over the Burnside River Valley, he contemplates:

> on this day I am beginning to see distant outlines of a totally different set of understandings. I want to think that travelling slowly and taking the land on its own terms, as we have done for the last six weeks, has allowed us to feel some of the same feelings and learn some of the same landscape-derived lessons as the original dwellers of this still and smokey valley.

It is fairly simple to separate each writer's sentiments from the object of his affectation. Nature accommodates such impositions. Yet the landscape has been transformed from place to personality, from space to specific function.)

The notion of an inviolable nature in which explorers and adventurers consort with destiny is an illusion. The narrative world, no matter how literally conceived, is invariably a matter of words. In fiction the landscape as narrative may be readily assessed in terms of textuality, but when the narrative is subservient to the Arctic it describes, as in most apparently nonfiction texts, authenticity is more elusive.

Everything written on the Canadian Arctic is, in effect, a northwest passage, the expression not only of the traditions but the geography and history of another world. The high north of our Canadian hemisphere is west of Eden, the Eurasian sources of our written language, and north of south, where the resources of our narrative heritage now reside. Eurocentricity, the empirical south, the cultural perspectives of a temperate linear world are built into the syntax of writing, the very shape of letters on the page. The Arctic is literally written down, even in the passages that most attempt to put it in its proper place.

The narratives of record by Hearne and Peary, the Arctic meditations of Barry Lopez, the elegiac evocations of Hugh Brody evade the conventions of literary criticism. It is necessary sometimes for the critic to leave books behind. It is essential sometimes for the critic to travel. Writing this in Mexico, I think more and more of Canada as a fictional device.

The more time I spend in the Arctic, the less sure I am about what I imagine it to be, even on the best authority.

Al Purdy wrote a poem about D. H. Lawrence at Lake Chapala, which is really a poem about Al Purdy at Lake Chapala; Purdy, shambling after Lawrence, trying to envision Lawrence on his knees, between bouts of writing, scrubbing the tile floor at Zaragoza #4, just down from where I had my car repaired; Purdy confronted again and again in his quest by death, the fey death of a bitching phoenix, which preys on words a bit, with moulting tail feathers; angry at the illimitable attenuation of his subject dying and, in spite of himself, honouring him with lamentation.

Purdy is troubled with the infinite, with seeing it through. In another poem he wonders if eternity goes forward or backward / or is it an ambiance? These words, in this particular arrangement, are his; without quotation marks. Later he talks of neverness, from Margaret Avison, with appropriate punctuation — and loses her. I'd prefer the risks of plagiarism to isolating the ineffable in time.

If all the world's a text, then everything we know and do is intertextual. Not only is life a metaphor but living it is plagiarism. But only if. There are ways out; there are ways back again.

Mackenzie River, the summer of 1989. In the late evenings by the light of the midnight sun, from Fort Simpson to the Beaufort Sea, Virginia and I read aloud the accounts of others who have camped on these ice-scarred shores before us. We read Mackenzie's journal, Franklin, Gary and Joanie McGuffin. But there is little to connect the places we read about and the terrain we are travelling through. The textual world is real enough, yet it seems to exist in parallel and not to intersect with our experience on the Deh Cho. Somehow, in being here, we have reached beyond words; through the rhythm of exhausted muscles, we have become part of northern landscape in ways no text, apparently, can apprehend.

The Big River, discovered by Mackenzie on his voyage to the Frozen Sea, is great and powerful, wide and often swift. It commands respect for the winds it channels into the face of northbound travellers and for thunderous standing waves it can throw up with little notice when winds and current clash. It is so earth-laden that sometimes grit will pepper the canoe like a thousand tiny drums and a person drowning would plummet to the bottom, weighted down by silt driven into the clothing's fabric. Ancestors of the Dene who paddled Mackenzie's canoes and felt the current in their own muscles, who cared for his party and suffered privation, had known the Deh Cho for millennia. Yet Mackenzie describes them with the same disinterest as he does the river. He is principally concerned with opportunities for trade.

Such were the imperatives of Mackenzie's expedition. But reading his narrative in a balmy endless setting of the sun, we wonder how the land could stay so much the same and he experience such a blind-side view of it. If the Mackenzie River Valley is represented in imagination by the writings of Mackenzie or Franklin or, nearly two centuries later, the McGuffins, then it is landscape bereft of majesty and beauty, of history, myth and even, tragically, of presence.

Travelling in the eastern Arctic, we have found the same discrepancy between apparently authentic renderings of landscape and the world perceived. Our readings of Jens Munk on Hudson Bay, Martin Frobisher on Baffin, Peary on Ellesmere and the polar ice cap, Amundsen on the Northwest Passage, or of Lopez, Wiebe, and Brody on the pan-Arctic panorama prepare us no better for what we find there than did the fiction of Yves Thériault or James Houston. Nor did such an artful reconstruction as *The Arctic Grail* — Pierre Berton brilliantly involves readers in the exploits of others, but his landscape is literary, discontinuous, and dramatic, the context of adventure, not its origin or cause.

Until we journey through the landscape literally with books in hand, we are unable to escape the world as text, aware only of unease between remembered readings of the Arctic and our own experience there.

At the ruins of Kittigazuit, just past the Delta on the Beaufort Sea, we find strange comfort in the confluence of written words and our experience in the drizzling rain, among moss-covered stone rings, upended driftwood tree trunks (some still supporting cross-members of phantom roofs), and a few graves, each contained by picket fencing of silver-weathered wood, the print on the markers barely legible.

There were a thousand people here once, Inuvialuit, before the U.S. whalers, the Russian iron trade. Missionaries. Influenza. Measles.

The words belong to Felix Nuyviak. Recorded by Nellie Cournoyea in 1976 and relayed by Rudy Wiebe to a wider readership in his 1989 contemplation of the north, *Playing Dead*, they are filled with apocrypha, describing the place where we are reading them, when he was a child at the turn of the century:

> From everywhere, people would arrive in Kittigazuit for the winter festivities. How many could there be? I do not know. I didn't know how to add, how to subtract then. But there were so many at Kitti and the opposite shore in the other village, Kukbak. Whenever they played games on the ice — a kind of soccer or rugby, the water would move and shake in the water holes. At night time, what a fury of light from all snowhouses. Lights generating from a soap-stone lamp and illuminating all the snowhouses. I liked to look from Kitti to Kukbak at night. These were our Christmas decorations and display of lights. Like now — here with our electric lights.

As we read this speaking of an elder, collapsed time opens around us immeasurable dimensions of place. Through memory caught in writing with humility, perhaps we can perceive meaning in landscape, instead of imposing it.

After Kittigazuit, we paddle the open restless sea toward Tuktoyaktuk, which remains for hours an elusive splinter on the far horizon. The artless accounts of Mackenzie, Franklin, and the McGuffins are behind us, and our own adventure is coming to an end. As we haul the last few miles, a modest revelation broaches clarity: the landscape might reveal as much about the literature of authenticity as does literature about the land. By the time we reach the Tuk Inn, have hot baths, and at midnight crack open the celebratory bottle of Saint-Emilion that we have carried all the way from Norman Wells, plans are roiling; the future, an awesome invitation.

We shall explore Hearne's narrative along the Coppermine, Frobisher's accounts on Baffin, even the legendary quietude of John Hornby on the Thelon. Stefansson and Rasmussen will come next; what will the landscape reveal, what desires and imperatives that textual analysis would leave obscured? And the greatest challenge — to read Robert Peary and other explorer-adventurers against actual experience on the polar ice cap. Here will be the chance to measure narrative in terms of the landscape it subsumes and to explore the landscape for what has been distorted or concealed. Such wondrous endeavour will shape the work of years to come.

At this point in my argument personality and polemics merge; the argument itself becomes narrative. My notes concern the authenticity of Arctic dreams, the intimations of mortality in Arctic writing. Mexico surrounds me, accommodating all my creature needs. I have learned to accept unchanging weather as a gift, to like the beer; I eat almost anything, sleep soundly at night, and my work goes well. It is easy to be an outsider in Mexico.

On a run through Ajijic with George, before he went back home to study, leaving Julia stoically distraught, I remember passing a cemetery filled with plastic flowers from the Day of the Dead, and from that I remember another grave site — on Bear Island in Temagami — and a tissue paper rose, the petals garnished with lipstick imprints, on a small fresh grave. And part of me is embarrassed by death and part of me is moved by the silent, garish gestures of affection and another part is stricken cold by the grace of conviction.

Summer 1991, the east shore of Baffin, a point of land called Pangnirtarluk, off Davis Strait. Pauloosie's vision fills the landscape. Standing in the sound of waves that crash among the boulders, with the light of evening in his eyes, he surveys the barren spit of rock-strewn ground at the mouth of North Pangnirtung Fiord where he and Kilabuk had lived for several years, from 1956. Three of their children were born here. They were very poor. "No tea," he says. "No sugar, no flour, no smoking." "Many seals," he says. He doesn't say *nattik*, but "seals." Now, as we wait for the wind to drop, he stands to see, then moves deliberately among the boulders, and stands again, and moves and stands again. He is comfortable with the revelations of arrested time, time occupied, immediate and areal, dimensioned like the landscape, not receding, in linear regression. There is something in his face approaching grace; serenity, yes, but more. Pleasure in the past; fulfillment, generosity. We feel no violation watching him.

Later he takes me on a tour of the site, stopping at a pile of rocks to explain in Inuktitut what happened there, then to another pile, then to a ring of stones to explain in Inuktitut that this was their home, and there another, and there another, three in all, then he takes me to a boulder tumble, to explain, although I do not understand Inuktitut, that from among the shadows by our feet they drew fresh water. We walk silently up the hillside, Pauloosie nimble among the boulders, me, in awkward imitation, to three small wooden boxes the size of orange crates in the lee of a large rock, resting among smaller rocks. "Baby," he says. He says the word three times, placing his open hand on each of the boxes in turn. Then he says, "1954." By the date I know they aren't his. And farther on, a larger box made of packing case boards; through the cracks, a skeleton. "Nineteen fifty-four," Pauloosie says. I know this to mean it had been here before he and Kilabuk arrived. From two splinters he fashions a cross, kneels on the hard earth and, with a stone hammer, mounts it against the box.

An hour later he takes Virginia, Laura, and Fred on the exact same route among the rocks, while I sit with Jacobee near the boat and we drink sweet tea. By late evening in the shadows of the midnight sun the wind drops and we skim the waves all the way to the head of the fiord, where Pauloosie and Jacobee drop us off and turn back toward Broughton Island with only the briefest gesture of goodbye.

It is often difficult in literal Arctic narratives to tell artfulness from art, to sort out rhetoric from chicanery and self-aggrandizement. Samuel Hearne took several decades turning his field notes into an enthralling story, himself into splendid fiction. Robert Peary related some of his most intimate adventures through the impersonal medium of a ghost-writer. Even the man who broke trail for Peary in 1909 to within 150 miles of the North Pole, Robert Bartlett, although probably the greatest ice captain of the century (possibly ever), a Newfoundlander, a distinguished explorer, author of three books, and a man of the highest integrity, was not above dissembling. Bartlett remained either silent or circumspect in details that might have compromised Peary's claims.

In an unrelated instance he clearly misrepresented the facts: as Harold Horwood points out in *Bartlett: The Great Canadian Explorer*, the Newfoundlander's harrowing account of the suffering and survival that followed the sinking of the *Karluk*, the Canadian Arctic Expedition ship virtually abandoned by Vilhjalmur Stefansson in 1913, confirmed the reports of those he saved in all details but one — the naming of an island to which he sent a reconnaissance party, who subsequently perished. Trying to obscure his possible error in judgement, Bartlett substitutes Wrangel Island in the Siberian Arctic for Herald Island in describing his orders — shifting accountability, shifting the landscape itself.

Bartlett received an award from the Royal Geographical Society for outstanding leadership in the *Karluk* disaster, and Stefansson, after leaving the ship near Herschel Island off the Mackenzie Delta, proceeded on the epic quest across the top of North America that would bring him such acclaim. Stefansson, perhaps because he wrote to a broader public than most explorers in this century, was among the most freewheeling with his facts, as he candidly confessed on a number of occasions. In a letter, once, he ingenuously declared that Roald Amundsen did likewise.

On the sea ice between Broughton Island and North Pangnirtung Fiord for thirty hours, hauling Pauloosie's boat with all our gear for the trek across Cumberland Peninsula, with a shore break for Spam sandwiches and a bit of sleep, we learn the art of emulation. Pauloosie and Jacobee leap ocean leads, wade through channels of slush, scramble across tilting chunks of ice, and never speak instruction to us. We mimic them exactly, for survival.

Man-hauling a boat across the crumbling sea ice to distant open water haunts me still with pleasures that I can't articulate but feel in memory as fulfillment, exhilarating as if the six of us were inextricably a part of everything we saw. On sea ice, in retrospect, entirely at home — visceral memory, reshaped by narrative, by words.

A Journey to the Northern Ocean, the account of Hearne's trek from Hudson Bay to the mouth of the Coppermine River between 1769 and 1772, is one of the great works of Arctic literature. It is not an historical artifact; it is history, but not history written merely to document the incursions of a remarkable man upon austere geography. It is a work of the imagination which, in many respects, overshadows the author's achievements as an explorer, naturalist, anthropologist, and agent of commercial enterprise.

Hearne's journals were not intended as notes for narrative. Personal experiences were matters of record. His perceptions of place consisted largely of distances, directions, and conditions. Yet in the project Hearne worked on until his death in 1792, he added anecdotes and interpolated descriptions of plant and animal life, of native culture and technology, and especially of the landscape. His scant few lines describing the mouth of the Coppermine River become a fulsome account of the banks, the current, the terrain. Hearne knew, perhaps intuitively, perhaps on advice, that narrative requires landscape. What his records and memory could not provide, research did.

Not incidentally, Hearne worked on his manuscript in close cooperation with a number of friends, including the man who ghosted Captain Cook's account of his third voyage and a notable biologist who specialized in Arctic America. But Hearne's genius was in bringing his notes and research together into an exceptional work of fancy, intellect, and enterprise in nearly perfect harmony. His *Journey* is, in many respects, a prototype of the Romantic ideal. The Shelleys and Lord Byron no doubt read Samuel Hearne or read about him. Mary Shelley certainly did before writing the opening and closing sequences of *Frankenstein*.

Guanajuato, early winter, 1990. Near the exit from the Museo de la Momias is a framed black-and-white photograph of five women, two of them in clothes suggesting the picture was taken around 1920. The other three are dead. All five stand against a wall; the living women have their arms around the propped-up corpses and they are smiling at the camera. The woman to the camera's left is naked and her skin hangs in rigid folds against her bones; her hair is full but unkempt. The woman to the right is wrapped in what appears to be a shroud or winding cloth; it is stained and worn through in places. The woman in the centre looks at first glance to be alive. She is wearing a wedding dress and her expression is serene, although the tilt of her head suggests distraction. From the way she is embraced in a standing posture by the other women, it appears that she weighs no more than ten or twenty pounds; her feet hardly touch the ground. Since the photograph, she has been arranged on a shelf behind glass and there is a baby lying beside her, apparently the cause of her death. In the photograph she seems more real; it has to do with context. All of her companions must be dead by now.

Before we leave Pangnirtarluk someone finds a rusting fox trap, sets it, throws pebbles to snap it, resets it, and Pauloosie, aged sixty-five, and Jacobee, aged fifty-six, chase each other around in skittering circles, snapping with the open trap at bums and testicles, taking turns as the attacker with each near miss, sliding on lichen, wheeling among boulders, laughing into the laughter echoing around us.

Hearne, in turning his adventures in the sub-Arctic and Arctic into art, is a precursor to Barry Lopez, whose celebrated *Arctic Dreams* places him, perhaps with Hugh Brody, foremost among what might be called the New Romantics. Lopez, especially, encapsulates the Arctic and its people, the flora, fauna, and geology, the light and air in a great holistic vision. So sensitive is he to the northern landscape, and so articulate that ultimately the Arctic seems an expression of his personality.

It is not ambition but the force of his rhetoric, the fluid power of his prose, that makes Lopez sometimes overwhelm his Arctic subject. Something similar often happens with journals of contemporary exploration and adventure — witness Robert Swan's *Icewalk;* or the *Polar Bridge* account — where pride not beauty overshadows landscape and the narrative becomes a celebration of personal achievement.

Rudy Wiebe, in *Playing Dead,* more modest and more intimate than *Arctic Dreams,* uses personality as a narrative device. His book is curiously disarming, a disjointed ramble through Arcticana, part diary, part documentary, with anecdotes and historical snippets, observations and fragments of historical analysis, poetic evocations, incantatory invocations, and philosophical conjecture held together by the author's voice and personal vision. Like Aritha van Herk and a handful of others, mostly poets, he envisions the Arctic as a sprawling metaphor, a mirror of southern realities and dreams. At the same time he allows it a separate integrity, implicitly acknowledging its existence prior to and apart from his perception of it. Wiebe meditating, speculating, mediating between past and presence, the Arctic and his readers, makes his book an exploration of interior landscape as much as of the Arctic world he endeavours to illuminate and share.

Purdy, in the postscript to his book of Arctic poetry *North of Summer*, writes: about the poems: they seem to me like a set of binoculars thru which you can view the Arctic from several thousand miles away. I'd prefer that the reader felt them to be an extension of his or her own eyes and mind. What I'm doing here is providing my own particular kind of optic glass.

Purdy's words admit, with humility and pride, the alien perspective of his written passages and, implicitly, the illimitable distance between his own realities and the world he writes about.

Among explorers and adventurers, impositions of familiarity, proprietary assumptions, commonly rise out of personal ambition. Stefansson privately expressed wounded pride that Amundsen and Bartlett would intrude into the Arctic as long as he still had an interest in it. Peary was more strident: anyone not Inuit found between or on the shores of eastern Ellesmere and western Greenland was publicly regarded as an interloper and a scoundrel, at least until Peary's business there was finished.

Peary's anger at Otto Sverdrup and arch-rival Dr. Frederick Cook for encroaching on his territory was commensurate perhaps with the furious drive essential to his enterprise. On one legendary occasion Peary wandered into Sverdrup's remote encampment on the coast of Ellesmere near Kane Basin and refused to stay for coffee. For a man of such vaunting pride it seems quite possible that when he could not reach by foot an arbitrary point on the polar ice he assumed sovereignty in imagination. He certainly knew the region better than any other man alive, Inuit or outsider. If desire is the measure, he deserved to attain the North Pole. Whether he did is still the subject of acrimonious debate.

Memories and oral histories, circumstantial evidence and disconnected artifacts disguise the actuality of Arctic high adventure. Nowhere in the world is corroboration as scant or circumspect. Nowhere do narrative and landscape, memories and death, so completely merge.

The many relics of Sir John Franklin's final expedition included bits of paper, once inscribed with print made illegible by weather and the innocent neglect of those who found them, and human remains in various states of deterioration and dismemberment. One skeleton, retrieved intact from the southern shore of King William Island by Charles Francis Hall in 1869, was eventually encased in oak and buried in the Painted Hall at Greenwich. The bones of Lieutenant H. D. T. Le Vesconte, as forensics discovered him to be, his flesh assimilated with the landscape a hemisphere away, ceased on burial to be artifacts.

Le Vesconte became instead a footnote, connecting tissue in the larger Arctic story that consumed him. His photograph in David C. Woodman's book *Unravelling the Franklin Mystery* commands the viewer's eye; he is not a pleasant-looking man. It is easy to imagine beneath the photo-frozen countenance a gleaming skull, beneath the curiously soft folds of his fingers, knuckle bones, and ligaments. He looks like a man who knew his duty; yet the rapt set of his mouth, the fixity of his eyes, suggest he suffered intimations that his death would be deprived of dignity. His face, his fate, as pictured here, say much of will, of fear, but nothing of ambition or desire.

For Peary the Arctic landscape was indistinguishable from aspiration, to endure forever. Other explorers, equally ambitious, treated the Arctic as an empty text in which to inscribe their names for posterity in narratives of their own design. Vilhjalmur Stefansson, a man of remarkable accomplishment (who changed his citizenship from American to Canadian, which he had been in the first place, in return for government support of his far-reaching explorations — as Bartlett later changed from British Newfoundlander to American in similar expectation of financial aid), admitted to the temptation — indeed, the necessity — of fabrication as part of the explorer's agenda. Sometimes it is necessary to become fiction, to become a fact.

Stefansson had no compunction about twisting his reputation into the heroic, downplaying the achievements of others, inventing dramatic adventures, and in at least one case writing a popular account of his exploits from someone else's notes (his description of the Mackenzie Valley and his travels north in *My Life with the Eskimo*, according to *Stefansson and the Canadian Arctic* by Richard Diubaldo, is largely drawn from Rudolph Anderson's private notes); this man was the source of major policy decisions on the part of government authorities.

Stefansson, like Peary, no less than Al Purdy, Farley Mowat, or Pierre Berton, rose to the necessity of imaginative re-creation. And what writers imagine the Arctic to be, that is what it has become — not in actuality, but in the minds of outsiders and increasingly of people native to the north. The imagined landscape of the Arctic, if not recognized unreal, will continue to be taken as reality itself.

Writing this in Mexico, in La Canacinta, reading and writing, rewriting the Arctic between runs along the beach and fajitas in Ajijic; alive among flowers, temperate weather, the languid sounds of an alien tongue, surrounded by cactus, arresting hills, an unforgiving past, by people saddened by history who celebrate death, carry guns against humans, and venerate lost causes; it is easy to lose perspective. I am surely not of this world, yet the Arctic I explore, the Arctic of words, is only a remnant , a morbid token at best. I must go home again, soon. The urgency is absolute.

3

THE CARTOGRAPHY OF DREAMS

*T*HE IMAGE THAT COMES first to mind is of darkness smouldering at the edges; the sky is obsidian and the snowbound earth in deep shadow, as smoking emanations of the early-morning wind excoriate the night. You cannot see your skis, yet. You are invisible; but the cold defines your extremities with precision. You can hear your heart beat through your veins, feel exhalation freeze against your face. The pellucid air turns gradually opaque; strengthening day obscures the universe, highlighting then obliterating the brightest stars.

You cut swiftly through the cold, hardly aware that you are moving. There is no limit between the snow and sky; the whirling ground wind blurs the edge of everything. You ski by instinct the intimations of a land without horizons; you inscribe the landscape with your mind. And as the dawning spreads, you begin to make out other skiers, skiing the same line; at first spectral figures, each hunched under a pack, then real and linked, cascading rhythmically across the frozen surface of the world.

This is the second morning skiing from the darkness into light. You don't care much about the race itself. But a visceral encounter with the soul, your spirit contiguous with landscape and the weather, that's another thing. The windchill is minus forty-one. You slept warm, though, bivouacked in snow, and opalescent visions of the night refuse to fade with the rising light of day. This is not the Arctic, even in imagination. But whatever of the Arctic landscape and its narrative transfiguration that so enthralls, the same is here.

Every outsider travelling the Arctic
becomes a writer
by default if not desire,
transcribing mental field notes
into memories inseparable from dreams
of writing, some written, others not;
and every writer of the Arctic is a traveller,
whether having travelled there
or not.

Read about the Arctic; the text
reads you —
that, by now, is understood;
the line between reader and written,
a convention, at best.
But the Arctic, too,
writes into reading
itself being read.

Most of what you will experience
when you enter Arctic landscape
has already happened.

You have only to imagine yourself
to be there.

When you encounter Arctic passages, it is difficult to sort your own
familiarity with the landscape, shaped by memories of previous reading or by dreams or empirical experience, from shared assumptions
looping through the language, gathering inchoate particulars of actual
or imagined journey into line. Conventions of the text precede,
determining how the wilderness is read; limits of narrative become the
boundaries of landscape, and grammar topography. Images of elsewhere define the terrain and make the alien appear accessible. The
imagined Arctic, shaped by the imperatives of the culture into which
it is being written, is only a reminder of what's real.

We're dealing here with the lie of the land, the nature of story,
with continuity, comprehension,
and the conventions of narrative.
We're dealing here with lines of language and culture,
personality, vision;
lines of containment, of connection,
routes and boundaries, dream lines and map lines,
lines of entry and escape;
the lines of landscape —
not geography, meridians, and parallels,
but river lines, shorelines, sastrugi,
horizons, fissures, and eruptions,
turns and bendings of the mind, of earth;
not planes and dimensions,
but the edges of planes, contours of dimension.
We're dealing here with the shaping of imagination,
upon entering alien terrain;
and the shaping of landscape
by imagination.
Whether you traverse the page, exploring
lines of narrative design, the dream lines
of another traveller,
or travel there yourself,
both writing and the land
precede you.

To put it another way, from a canoe the land is always rising. You
paddle flooded folds on the surface of the Earth, in a quest for closure,
the completion of a line to be drawn across the lowest courses of
encountered terrain. But the land is prophetic; in its contours, your
journey predetermined. You follow, rapt in romance; the landscape
does not follow you. On a map you run the lines from noun to noun
as you extend the boundaries of the landscape you imagine travelling.

That's a beginning, but not the complete equation;
one premise in a syllogism.

The canoe is also useful in the revelation of dreams.
The landscape, articulate, in shaping desire.

The greatest Arctic narrative was silence. John Hornby, educated at Harrow, of impeccable breeding and excellent connections, articulate, obsessed (surely the marks of a great explorer), enthralled with the mortification of his own flesh (his life random slash marks across the tundra), we know him only through the records of others, and from the occasional sketch and grainy photograph. It is the silence of this strange small man that haunts nearly every narrative of the Barrens since his arrival, early in this century, and his death by deprivation in 1927.

It is the words that Hornby did not write, did not publish, the account he neglected to offer of himself and the harrowing years in a wilderness he embraced with ferocity, his refusal to accept that story lines, map lines, the connections between where he was from and where he was going were of any importance at all, his refusal of linearity, even when it meant his inevitable death — the only record of which would be the heroic and callow asides of his sacrificed nephew, who left the narrative of their passing in the cold ashes of an extinguished fire — his refusal to extricate his dreams from the landscape, to enter with words the continuum of history and geography, culture and kindred conscious-ness, it is his absence of voice that makes Hornby's vision the ineluc-table limit for others, writing of their own adventures to the edges of the same territory.

George Whalley, a distinguished Coleridgian and an Englishman in everything but birth, wrote a careful and at times inspired account of Hornby's life, trying to put this man of lesser talent and elusive brutish aspirations into words. And the irony, of course, is that Hornby now is a narrative device, subject to textual analysis like any other literary construct; a character, a metaphor, a thrilling motif.

Until George died, his notable service in British intelligence and his modest legacy as a gentleman of letters matters of record, I know well enough he envisioned the Barrens with Hornby in mind, the land and the man as inseparable. And if Coleridge, for Whalley, embodied perversely the culture that made him, that he, in turn, helped to remake, then Hornby, for Whalley, was the land that obsessed him, the enthralled embodiment of an outsider's Arctic — and, in turn, the landscape, the beautifully bleak and illimitable Barrens, was the perfect analogue for a manic and depressive English mind: Whalley's mind; Hornby's; the attenuated sensibilities of both men finding refuge, even compensation, in the Arctic, the sub-Arctic terrain.

How do you separate a man from his story?
How do you tell the silence of women from the stories of their lives?
Why is the Arctic a landscape ineffable, except as the expression of manhood,
in metaphors that tell of trials,
encounters, that mutter by rote the catechism of gender and race?

How do you inscribe the ineffable, how do you write it down? The epitaph for John Keats was writ on water; how do you put water into words? How do you draw the line, except on snow, that marks your presence, passing, and connects you with the seasons and the landscape? How, when winter fades, can you tell where you have been?

In a brilliant example of metafiction that rivals John Barth's "Lost in the Funhouse" as narrative discourse on the problematics of fiction, Rudy Wiebe's "Where Is the Voice Coming From?" may be said to valorize the procedures of writing over the written text as an autotelic code — so much for that; the critic talking to critics. Words connect, but they also circumscribe and exclude, separate and divide. Where in the rhetoric is the death of Almighty Voice, the young warrior at the centre of Wiebe's narrative; he is lost among the implements of an academic discipline, his story obscured by professorial cant. The professors are angry, as Virginia Woolf said, and they don't know they are angry. That makes their anger dangerous.

In *Writing a Woman's Life*, Carolyn G. Heilbrun uses chilling eloquence to articulate a simple truth: the script in which to tell a woman's story is only now being written into women's lives. Inevitably the professors are angry; even more so than before.

In slower stretches water bends and you coast the downhill slide; in swifts you ride the broken waters easily; in rapids you whirl and eddy with the water's fall — but always, even as you career across the landscape, you see solidity above; rocks ahead, beside and pressing through the surge below, are ephemeral, not really land at all but the effects of light or dangerous anomalies in the river's flow.

Or as the waters rise against you, as you haul against the current — then, too, the world above is solid and, beneath, slips by as bottom shadows in a fractured stream.

Or in still water where the displacement of your craft keeps you afloat, you shape words to hold the landscape in place, a necessary border to the world.

From a canoe, the rising landscape is always threatening,
or promising,
to fall away.

> At eleven p.m. [Wednesday, August 10, 1825] we arrived at Fort Good Hope, the lowest of the Company's establishments; it is distant from Fort Norman three hundred and twelve miles, and is in latitude 67°28′21″ N., and longitude 130°51′38″ W.,: the variation of the compass being 47°28′41″ E.

These precise notations are from the narrative of the enterprising John Franklin, at this time a captain in the Royal Navy, serving imperatives he describes as "important to the naval character, scientific reputation, and commercial interests of Great Britain," on his second expedition to the shores of the Polar Sea, in spite of the perceived "humane repugnance of His Majesty's Government" to his previous expedition to the mouth of the Coppermine, in which half the company of twenty perished.

The genial character of Franklin's account is periodically interspersed with such readings of established points, proving them through celestial divination to be precisely where they are; connecting them mathematically to where he has come from and where he is going; fixed points within his narrative, increments on his journey between anticipation and achievement, from England abroad and to England again.

Barry Lopez in *Arctic Dreams* says maps are an expression of what we wish the landscape to become, an elegant transliteration of our will to order. We draw lines, according to rule, to extend the boundaries of what we already know — Mercator as metaphor, and the map a marauder, the ensign of sovereign design.

Arctic Dreams is a map, charting random particulars at the northern edges of the known world. And just as constellations reduce stellar depths to figures in an optic sky, so narrative gives perspective priority, and renders the infinite a realistic motif. With lyric grace Lopez writes himself into landscape, and the Arctic becomes a flourish on the margin of the chart of the writer's contemplation of himself.

Constellations are plot summaries,
or, another way of seeing it, maps,
bringing the infinite to a single plane
and eternity into line.
Beyond Cassiopeia and the Pleiades, the universe sprawls
unbound — when viewpoint is view, the splendours of chaos
become souvenirs of the Earth.

Exploration of the Arctic by ship, recorded in a ship's log or private journal; entry and progress by lake and river, noted in a field book; or over snow, recalled in memoirs, re-created in fiction; entry into northern wilderness on solid earth, drawn neatly into narrative illusion — reveal a multiplicity of worlds that converge only through accidents of language and imagination. How landscape impinges on consciousness is subject to critical analysis, but how the structures of human consciousness re-create the land varies infinitely. Every experience of the Arctic is unique; every rendering of it into words the cartography of private dreams.

In the best of Arctic writing our estrangement from the natural world yields to atavistic convolutions of the text that connect us, as outsiders, directly to the land — words evoke nostalgia for a world remembered by its absence. It is not, however, that wilderness has been made domestic, the feral subdued, but that art has breached the barriers between language and experience, imagination and the world imagined. The achievement, remarkable in letters, leaves the landscape untouched.

Imagine skiing a race that never ends, because in the cerebral exertion of muscle to accord with the shape of the land and the visceral flow of your mind, moving from darkness to light over the swift terrain, the linearity of time is confounded by the illimitable extension of space, and the limits of place by the refusal of time to fall into line. Imagine the words, to share this with others; to fix the ineffable and make it familiar.

Imagine Arctic landscape:
listen, the quietude echoes an absence;
you are elsewhere and the Arctic
is a silent movie in your mind.
Look up; against the sky
a single figure, exposed
through the hard season
of your imaging;
an inukshuk,
stones
held by gravity in human shape,
defines your field of vision;
the lens zooms, swings,
reaching for stasis,

but even still
the picture flickers;
freeze-framed,
the film
still moves.

You do not imagine a photograph
unless it is a photograph you are imagining.

One:
inukshuk.
Now imagine two:
inukshuuk,
the length of perception
between them, on rocky promontories
separated by indeterminate terrain,
say tundra, water, windscape;
say windscape, the word
shrieks, whispers,
rumbles with the grinding of boulders,
the petulant rustle of flowers,
with the melting of snow, the drift
of glacial ice, the wheeling sky;
the mindscape rumbles
with language,
opening credits flash from sight
and cinematographic
magic
overwhelms the viewer;
you are nowhere, neither there
nor where you are. You are
on one side or another
of the line between stone figures in your mind,
within a field defined
only by the limits
of what you see.

You do not imagine yourself
without imagining where
in the world
you are.

Imagine many: inukshuit.
Each stone figure centred in its own terrain;
from each to every other
a line extends and taken all in all
the permutation of their pairings
like a topographic grid
holds the landscape in place,
a dreamscape fixed
like a holograph
approaching perfection
in the wandering mind.

You do not imagine the world
unless you imagine your absence
among its particulars.

Only connect: I stare at the painting of George Douglas in his book *Lands Forlorn*. It is the frontispiece and very flattering — I know this because several candid photographs in the book show him less strikingly handsome although of more character, looking out at us from an age when the appearance of character was nearly everything. Almost a cliché, with his piercing blue eyes, rich brown hair, and luxuriant moustache, he looks like what I imagine my grandfather Austin must have been, judging from a black-and-white photograph my father used to have on his dresser, also dating from before the Great War. Both men in their pictures are significantly younger than I am now.

Among George Douglas's many photographs from his prewar winter on Great Bear Lake are several shadowy images of John Hornby. Hornby is familiar in a much-reproduced 1919 photograph, slim as a rake, hirsute in the country style, wearing moccasins, sitting on a log, thumbing through an Eaton's catalogue. In Edgar Christian's diary *Unflinching*, published a decade after both men had perished on the Thelon, the same snap appears beside a drawing of Hornby, identified as Jack, his cheeks clean-shaven, hair neatly brushed, an open-necked shirt fading into the flatness of sketch paper, lips pursed between a strongly set chin and aquiline nose, with a close-cropped moustache, strained jawline bled into pencilled shadows behind him and, most remarkably, the sad pale eyes of a visionary. He, too, reminds me of my grandfather. Hornby's unwritten book on the Barrens was to be called "In the Land of Feast or Famine; or, A Life in the Arctic Region." It is hard both to live with visions and write them down. Hornby's words were lost somewhere along the Thelon.

The full-body photograph of Harold Adlard, who also died there with Hornby and his nephew, looks like someone I know. It takes up the whole of page 57 in George Whalley's edition of *Unflinching*, called *Death in the Barren Ground*. I'd swear it was Dick Livingstone, a guy I used to hang around with when we were kids in Blair. He taught me how to snare rabbits and, once, to steal chickens (a chicken). He died in a car crash in 1955. Adlard seems to be leaning against a flagpole that isn't there, or holding up a mug of tea, although his hand is empty. He looks straight at the camera, squinting into the light and smiling with his mouth open, as if, in the cold, he can't quite get his breath. He reminds me of me, if I had been there, standing in the snow in a light shirt, wearing oxfords, not quite framed by a hand-split door the shape of a coffin.

There are other faces, in various accounts of the Barrens, that remind me of my grandfather, that remind me of myself. There is no connection, however, with the one photograph available of Edgar Christian. In the washed tones and pale shadows he seems a school-boy, from another age when such a word could still be used. His retouched picture, like the words of his diary, reveal him to be ingenuous and without complexity; a perfect foil perhaps for Hornby; a perfect witness to the death Hornby pursued with manic determination. I feel for Christian, the boy-hero as he came to be known for the dispassionate manner of his dying, but I do not identify with him. He is of my grandfather's age and somehow has not passed over into ours.

Edgar's distant cousin was Fletcher Christian, who was a schoolboy with William Wordsworth. Edgar let the fire dwindle to exhaustion; then he placed his diary and letters home inside the icy stove before retiring to his bunk to die. He might well have written, not as did New England whaling captains in their logs, And So Ends This Day, but rather, And So Ends This Life. From the composure of his closing words it seems doubtful he grasped the implications of his pathetic passing.

Skiing from Lachute to Gatineau, the same trail every year for 170 kilometres that conditions alter radically from gruelling slough to frozen ruts (and sometimes it is perfect); skiing the Gold Coureur de Bois, a little embarrassed by the label, proud of the distinction; skiing the Canadian Ski Marathon, the most demanding loppet in the world; for one weekend, prepared for, dreamed about, committed to, you set yourself to challenge limits, to reel in the open spaces of a transcendental episode in ordinary time.

Sedentary colleagues wonder why I do it; certain members of my family worry. It's right at the edge of my capacity to achieve, and several times I haven't made it — once through hypothermia (I knew I knew I knew my name, but it took me half an hour before I could put the words to it) and, in 1992, from rough conditions, exhaustion, and frozen toes (threatening to cast me in the company of Robert Peary and Peter Freuchen, who both lost nether digits to their polar obsessions, although I only lost the nails and the odd gouge of extraneous flesh). Still, I dream of skiing again that same undulating line across the variety of tumultuous and pastoral terrain; next year is another event in the same race.

You do these things, extend yourself to the limits of what the mind and muscles will endure, because there, while there, boundaries bend, borders blur. This is not a question of transcendence through morti-fication of the flesh. It is an honouring of the body as landscape, for the endurance athlete becomes the thing being done, becomes the landscape of its doing. It is not denial but affirmation. Transcendence, yes, but through the extension of personality, not its abnegation.

Imagine wilderness; imagine skiing or running; or walking. Imagine time passing and your goal, effectively, the end of time. The horizon forms a line at the edge of your perception. Imagine running toward the horizon; a line of hills, or better, plane on plane of hills, like a Chinese painting. You will never reach the horizon, of course, but time will end just the same. Now, imagine yourself, with humility born from the depths of commitment, inseparable from the land — the horizon no longer a personal affront, the boundary of consciousness; it is a promise, the affirmation of an unseen but substantial world extending without limits, forever. Imagine yourself, now, in motion, running, or skiing, or walking; you are movement, the land in motion. There is no end to anything.

There
says an old Inuk hunter
at home
within the circle of stones
he knows
from the old days
according to Norman
whose thoughts on the Arctic
are highly regarded
in appropriate circles
(who is now telling us
over lunch)
there he says turning
is Cambridge Bay there
Igloolik there
Cape Dorset there
Lake Harbour there

Rankin there
Resolute there
Gjoa Haven we are at the centre of these
here. This is not a poem. It is Norman's story:
we are at the centre of these
says the Inuk elder
to the gathered circle
at an Ottawa luncheon
(although he has never been
to most of the places
he names
in person).

Virginia and I, paddling the Dumoine, late in the summer of 1991: the river surface falls away at each dramatically articulated set of rapids. The banks, some in subtle retreat from the ragged shore and others soaring to a thousand feet, rise over us in erratic waves as the falling waters coax and hurl our canoe through one notch after another on the river's southward drive toward the Ottawa.

In deep slow chasms intervening and the shallow swifts between we talk of maps and dreams; a sporadic conversational rehearsal for more flamboyant journeys farther north: the Thelon, the Coppermine, the Hood, the Missinaibi. Sometimes the water's falling thunder swallows up our words, and every muscle fibre, nerve, and cell is focused on our reading, urgently, the river as text, reiteration of the planet's raucous past. We paddle and portage, plot and plunge through receding terrain, scheduled to be off the Dumoine and on the Ottawa by Sunday afternoon.

On May 6, 1992, Robert Martel, described in the press as an American explorer, was rescued from the polar ice cap near Ward Hunt Island and flown to nearby Alert, the Canadian military base on the north end of Ellesmere, for debriefing and resuscitation. It seems he had struck out on his own from the Weber-Malakhov expedition, leaving the eponymous pair to explore the Pole without him. Martel was discovered, after four days of intense searching, making his way homeward. According to radio reports, he may not have known he was lost.

Sometimes the editors of Time-Life, Incorporated, seem in charge of the world; sometimes *Reader's Digest.*

Book-of-the-Month Club judges named *Kabloona,* by Gontran de Poncins, their selection for April 1941.

At one point in his described adventures de Poncins was travelling by sled with an Inuk called Ohohunuak and says, "what with moving through every point of the compass" among a cluster of islands, "it became clear that we were lost."

Ohohunuak, however, rested, had a pipe, said "Na-ma-kto," which means "very good," and they started again and followed the line of an island riverbed until the overshot coastline came in sight, then turned back on the coast until they encountered lines in the snow, sled tracks leading where they wanted to go.

In "that obscure consciousness," as de Poncins brutally characterizes the Inuit mind, Ohohunuak did not know he was lost.

The author proclaims, "There is no fiction in this book." As if the alternative were truth.

Was it the information industry that brought Farley Mowat to the land of the Ihalmiut, following his bloody years (with my father) overseas? Was it encapsulated culture that impelled him to formulate *People of the Deer* as a metaphor of public values (shaped on the model of a nineteenth-century boy's novel)? Whatever the intricate web of desire that led to his Arctic experience, or the diverse social imperatives that shaped versions of this experience into a reassuringly derivative text (with echoes of R. M. Ballantyne, my father's favourite, and *Chums,* of Jules Verne and James DeMille, of Herman Melville, Margaret Mead, and Peter Freuchen), such are the factors and forces through which we as his readers connect to the landscape of his narrative design, and are kept from the land itself.

In his introduction Mowat vows like a Rider Haggard hero to hurtle back through time into a prehistoric past and across a perilous and empty space where he will discover and champion a lost tribe of benighted primitives. Ingenuously he merges the motivation for his sojourn at the tundra's edge with the rhetorical intent of his narrative: to do, to write, and to read of doing are much the same. He thus becomes the reader's champion, as well. And so effectively does the storyteller's art transform "the desperate people" and their homeland into the material connection between writer's passion and reader's response, the text supersedes reality. The Ihalmiut and their place in the world become matters of imagination, their plight an expression of the author's empathy, the reader's conscience.

Experience inevitably finds its measure in the expectations of those who seek to establish its limits.

Consider the words of Hugh MacLennan: "Above the 60th parallel you feel that no-one but God has ever been there before you."
Consider the note by John Richardson to his fellow explorer George Back while surveying the Arctic coast on the Franklin Expedition in 1821: "Nowhere did I see anything worthy of your pencil. So much for the country. It is a barren subject, and deserves to be thus briefly dismissed."
And consider the words of Gontran de Poncins:

> This was the Arctic tundra, a land indescribable because there is literally nothing to describe, nothing that holds the eye, that exalts, that gives promise of anything whatever at the end. If there is a landscape in the world in which no thrill of romance can be evoked, it is this.

De Poncins's description elsewhere of the Arctic people as being indistinguishable from the land is ineptitude of sensibility, for he does not mean they are at home in their environment but rather that they are incidental to his experience of it, as "colorless," he notes, "as the tundra itself."

In the Time-Life edition of *Kabloona*, published in 1965, reprinted in 1980, the editors of *Time* endorse the notion: "one cannot exchange ideas with an Eskimo.... Properly speaking the Eskimo does not think at all."

But consider also the well-meaning words of Warburton Pike, a sportsman who in the late 1880s travelled north in search of musk ox to kill for sport: "To the man who is not a lover of Nature in all her moods the Barren Ground must always be a howling, desolate wilderness. . . ." He liked this wild world he characterizes in the feminine. And consider the words of another sportsman, David Hanbury, writing in 1904: "to the natural features of the country it would be difficult for any writer to do justice.... The Northland must be lived in to be understood and appreciated, for its constantly changing aspect baffles description."

Pike and Hanbury, both hunters, both enthralled with the sub-Arctic wilderness, envision it empty of people. The connections they make, the lines they draw are rhetoric; literary, aesthetic, and moral. The lines of their knowing do not intersect with lines of the people, the life lines and dream lines, the lines of landscape and seasons. Such minds look at a landscape on which there are no people at a given time and say, "there are no people on this land," as if demographics and survey lines are sovereign measures, taking precedence beyond ancestral dreams. They do not understand the landscape as genetic celebration; dreams of the landscape, waking the dead.

It is difficult to distinguish underlying assumptions in the structures of imagination when the architecture is your own design.

Consider Stefansson's statement in *My Life with the Eskimo:* "Take the
Eskimo out of his habitual surroundings and he is, as a general thing,
far inferior of the white man in finding his way about." You have to
wonder, what did he expect? Where does the anger come from that
perceives the world in vertical configuration, and affinity with nature
an affront?

Imagine running on the gravel road from Arctic Bay to Nanisivik;
if you follow down the Crunch to the Nanisivik dock
on Strathcona Sound, and up again to the town site
in the lee of Mount Fuji,
you will have covered forty-two kilometres;
do it twice and you've done the Midnight Sun Ultramarathon.

In 1991 Don McNally and Virginia took off down the Crunch
at 4:00 a.m., running into gale force winds and sleet;
two hours later the official start was put on hold,
and later the course was changed to include the Crunch five times
    over,
so that runners could be monitored from Nanisivik for hypothermia
and rescued if necessary by truck, the mine helicopters being tied up
recovering fifty-six Inuit adrift on ice floes off Pond Inlet.

Running the steep incline of the Crunch five times,
five k up and five k down,
always in sight of other runners pushing either way,
five k up and five k down;
I look amid the photographs, scattered through my mind,
at my maternal grandmother, snapshots and portraits
superimposed on the landscape,
chiaroscuro monuments against the Arctic sky.

Isabelle Cameron. 1867–1968. Isabelle Clare.
I listen to her voice in the calming wind; over and over,
Ontario Scotch re-echoing the German accent of her in-laws,
"Chust do-itt; chust do-itt; chust do-itt." But I can only see

photographs in which she becomes the landscape;
I can only see the landscape.

Running the gravel road on Baffin Island
I haven't forgiven my mother for dying.
Running the gravel road on Baffin Island
I forgive my mother for dying.

Sometimes it seems anger in the Western world must be of ancient lineage; the Hebrew prophets, Aristotle, and an endless succession of popes maintained our fledgling species, apparently made for higher things, would float incorporeal above the earth were it not that woman's womb provides material matter in which the ascendant human spirit dwells. Such rendering of reality as masculine metaphor leaves only fear to live with, for men and women both, or fury, as grace allows.

When Leonidas Hubbard wrote his final words, as he lay dying barricaded in a tent against the autumn snow of Labrador, due east of Disappointment Lake, he assumed closure on the article he was devising for an American men's adventure magazine. It was 1903. He did not know that Dillon Wallace, one of his two companions, would write a bestselling yarn, *The Lure of the Labrador Wild*, and turn his suffering, and his intransigence as a leader, into mythic misadventure.

Affecting regional idiom, addressing the reader directly, Dillon Wallace, the urban lawyer, salutes his fallen comrade:

> Bravo, Hubbard! nothing could down your spirit for long, could there? So high was your spirit that you could not know it was impossible for your poor old body to hold it any longer. Your hand was firm when you wrote, b'y, speaking eloquently of that which most of all was you. "It is a man's game," you said one day, in referring to our desperate struggle to reach those we loved. Well, you played it to the limit, b'y, and it was a man's death. My friend, I am proud of you.

Such men knew Rudyard Kipling by heart, and believed him.

Wallace showed an astonishing commitment to the recovery of Hubbard's remains; his popular account of transporting the frozen corpse lashed to a sleigh must surely have inspired Robert Service a few years later to build his funeral pyre for Sam McGee. The narrative of his survival led Hubbard's young widow, a feisty Canadian, furiously indignant at her husband's death, to race against Wallace on her own epic trip by canoe across central Labrador in 1905, guided by the other survivor of the Hubbard tragedy, George Elson, a Cree from James Bay.

Mina Hubbard. As tough an Arctic explorer as ever held the field. Yet her account, *A Woman's Way Through Unknown Labrador,* measures out the stages of her grief, like the stations to Golgotha, as she reaches for a parity of being with Leonidas, her heroically dead husband. Look at Mina Hubbard's photograph.

Consider Mina Hubbard; where is she in the text of Arctic exploration; where is she among the vast accumulated store of words on epic adventure in the northern wilderness? What does all the writing teach us, what does it profess, when Mina Hubbard is at best a footnote to her boyish husband's exemplary demise?

Look at Mina Hubbard's photograph. The caption describes her in "hiking" attire. She is in the heart of lethal wilderness, carrying a rifle, striding toward the camera, calmly suppressing a smile, her Edwardian skirt kicked high enough you can see her ankles, her boots, her shadow in the midday sun. She is not on a hike.

Virginia Woolf :
the professors are angry. They don't know
they are angry and that makes
their anger
dangerous. To everyone,
she might have said, although she was talking
in that particular instance of women.

Talking to women at Cambridge,
a few of them professors themselves
or nearly professors. Professors
are dangerous to women.
Editors, too.
Critics are dangerous;
critic-professors who edit,
as dangerous
as anthropologists;
as dangerous as explorers
of the Arctic
who write the Arctic down.

Look at Mina Hubbard's portrait. A charcoal background shows her
pale complexion strong in outline; her hair is rich and finely textured;
around her throat, a pearl choker; at her breast, an ornate broach; and
rising from her lap, an open rose.

Look at the photograph of Mina in England, on the day of her
marriage to Harold Ellis in 1908. It is in a book called *Great Heart:
The History of a Labrador Adventure*. She was Mina Hubbard for such
a short time. She looks straight into the camera; you can see only
shadows where her eyes must be.

The Western world is prepossessing; its anger runs the parallels.
To the north of its course, to the south, the assumptions of primacy
by virtue of nature, of history, supersede alien realities, subsume
them, make them aberrant extensions of the traveller's home. Aritha
van Herk identifies Ellesmere as a woman on the verge of flesh, and
merges herself and the island with Anna Karenina. In *Places Far
from Ellesmere* she writes her defiance of Tolstoy and the angry
Western world.

Every outsider travelling the Arctic
becomes a writer
by default if not desire,

and every writer of the Arctic is a traveller,
away from home.

In her book of essays *In Visible Ink* van Herk discovers herself on
sinuous ocean ice between Resolute and Grise Fiord as invisibled by
awe. The conceit is metaphysical, deconstructing on the page to make
her point (the hypothetical intersection of consciousness and icescape,
occupying no space):

> I am quite simply unable to write of or through this polar spell.
> Instead, it inscribes me, takes over my cullible imagination and
> its capacity for words: invents me for its own absent-minded
> pleasure. Effaces any referentiality, a transformation without
> continuity or chronology.

In *The People of the Twilight*, published in 1928, Diamond Jenness
suggests that for the Inuit, "religion and hysteria went closely hand in
hand." In the preface to the same book, explorer and Norwegian
statesman Fridtjof Nansen extends his concern for native peoples of
the world to include the Inuit :

> Let there be no doubt about it; they, too, are doomed if nothing
> really effective is done to protect them. The land of the great
> white silence will never more ring with the happy mirth of these
> lovable children of the twilight.

The Arctic for both men is a mirror: perspective mistaken for perception; experience for reality.

There is a curious distancing in the writings of Jenness and Nansen
from the landscape of the Arctic, given that one of them professes to
an understanding of its people, and the other of its character. Drawing
in his book *Farthest North* on ancestral Nordic imagery, Nansen
envisions the Arctic a slumbering giant, waiting to be aroused by forays
from the south. Jenness avoids such enervating metaphors; he writes
a crisp, efficient prose to make science accessible. The pride and

purpose of both men comes of their being from somewhere else; outsiders by profession in an alien world. Jenness, who seems surprised that "The Eskimos themselves knew nothing of days and weeks; they kept no reckoning even of the months, only of the changing seasons," spent much of his time with the Canadian Arctic Expedition in 1913–16, measuring the circumference of Inuit heads. He was, for years, an anthropologist with the Canadian Geological Survey and the Canadian National Museum in Ottawa.

Like Gontran de Poncins, like Farley Mowat, like Peter Freuchen in *The Book of the Eskimos*, Vilhjalmur Stefansson in *My Life with the Eskimo*, or Knud Rasmussen, himself part Inuit, writing on the Fifth Thule Expedition, all writing in the first half of this century, Jenness draws lines of knowledge, of sovereignty, and of intent to separate the native peoples from their natural environment (even present terminology divides — the notion of environment itself suggests the possibility of separation). Mowat describes "the desperate people," without apparent irony as "squatters in this land of ours." (Remember Joseph Howe's memorial line, "For ages thus the Micmac trod our soil," which was written a century before?) Metonymic territoriality; the expression of cultural imperatives, no less damning for being well-meant.

In such writing are peoples dispossessed. Due as much to prehistoric origins as to cultural discontinuity, making them intruders from a primeval and therefore inauthentic past, native kinship with the land, as with humanity, is denied. Map lines are placed around the landscape, boundaries inscribed to contain them; studies detail their habits, to remind us of our differences — but there are seldom lines to connect their worlds with the writers' own. Inevitably, even Rasmussen, in-formed by the cultural traditions of both worlds, failed to connect.

Anthropology: the bastard offspring of colonialism. It's almost too easy to write. A solipsistic palimpsest — the old text inscribed with the line of its heirs, the new anticipating its own past. Typological gossip.

(Words, written, like walnuts within the fist of a single thought, in static collision resist, conflate, hard edges set against each other penetrate, explode; the fingers open to reveal strange configurations of meat and shards, to be picked over leisurely, separated sometimes from strings of blood and creases on the skin.)

Mina Hubbard's story begins with her husband's dream of adventure in Labrador and ends with her second marriage, in England. Surely someone, having read Carolyn G. Heilbrun, or lived as a woman, will write her into the life she deserves, or at least the one she endured.

Inukshuk, inukshuuk, inukshuit.
Inuk.
Inuuk.
Inuit.
One is solitude; you cannot tell a resting figure from the ground.
A couple, continuity; nothing is entirely at rest in the living world.
More, community; the world, alive.

Numbers are without meaning when everything is holy, because nothing is absent. If you understand this, then you know the importance of lines: that unity lies in the inviolability of diverse connections. In such a world you can never be lost — for the line you make, a solitary figure in motion, whether actual or in your dreams, or merely through time, will inevitably intersect with other lines. Singularity is an illusion. You have no limitations.

Running through Croydon, on the way from Westminster Bridge to Brighton beach, October 1991. Running through Croydon, I look for my grandfather. It is a dawning Sunday morning, cool and surprisingly quiet, with the muffled hush of a city street still damp from the night. A 180 runners already spread over several miles attract little notice. The only witnesses are early risers attending other matters. I cannot see my grandfather, but above the neon shop fronts I see Victorian facades that must have been exactly so before he left as a young man a hundred years ago for Canada.

Running the Croydon High Street, dreaming another man's life, a lifetime ago. Dreaming of Austin; knowing him better perhaps than if we had met. Breaking finally out of greater London into landscape shaped and sculpted like a giant country garden. (He arrived in Canada, went north, then south; had several pictures taken; lived another thirty years; and died.) Grieving in exhilaration; genetically extravagant, and still in mourning.

Before Austin joined my Canadian forebears he briefly affirmed being English among the Maori in New Zealand and then as a scout in the Boer War. By the time his genes entered the Mohawk-Mennonite-Scotch-Bavarian-English pool from which my own derive, in Preston, Ontario, Croydon had become more a part of him, through longing, than if he'd never left. So I've been told. He didn't write; his legacy was the maze of rumours that still reverberates with the echoes of his passing. On the way to Preston he travelled the sub-Arctic, even while his mind was fixed among the gingerbread houses of Croydon and the fairy-tale oaks of Surrey, where trees are strategically isolated for aesthetic impact, without underbrush or hedgerows to connect them. What did he make of wilderness, of the Barrens? Although he never wrote about it, he loved the Canadian high north with a sadness, it is said, that was fierce and unforgiving.

There is apparently in Antarctica a place called the Pole of Relative Inaccessibility. Sometimes you can't avoid taking geography personally. Sometimes it is necessary; the inexorable culmination of everything you might have been.

Knud Rasmussen recorded the following on the Fifth Thule Expedition between Greenland and Siberia:

> True wisdom is only found far away from people, out in the great solitude, and it is not found in play but only through suffering. Solitude and suffering open the human mind, and therefore a shaman must seek his wisdom there.

Rasmussen transcribed what my grandfather wanted to hear.

There is an inscription beneath the statue of Robert Falcon Scott in Christchurch; his dying words, about how once again Englishmen were proving they could meet death with unflinching grace. He went south as far as it is possible to go and died on the retreat. His body, encapsulated in the vast Antarctic ice mass with his companions, all but Captain Oakes still inside their tent, drifts slowly northward. Eventually a chunk of ice will shear off and follow ocean currents toward New Zealand, perhaps farther, wandering as it thaws until at last the remains of "Scott of the Antarctic" and his friends will be delivered to the ocean floor, their flesh fresh as the day they died.

Death makes even the most austere landscape intimate. Consider Scott or young Edgar Christian; consider Leonidas Hubbard. The clarity of their words as each died from freezing and starvation makes no attempt to distance them through indignation, mourning, or distraction from the landscape of their imminent destruction. Each took advantage of malingering death to write notes home. Their words seem hardly concerned with the landscape that embraces them; their words reach out, across an ineluctable divide, to connect the places of their heart, the times of their life, with the moment of their suffering and death. The landscape, they accept as their final companion; and the landscape, at least for a time, contains them.

Scott's statue in Christchurch looks like plaster of paris, although it is simply weathered. Braced against a single ski pole, he stares valiantly into the trees. Scott is at the centre of what is known in the history of Antarctic exploration as "the heroic age," when suffering was equated with manliness (just as it once offered access to God; and now offers proof of the sufferer's common humanity). The measure of heroic suffering, the apotheosis of manhood, was not in what the suffering was for, but in how much was endured, and how well. Scott; Hornby; Hubbard. And, of course, Franklin, around whom heroic death was virtually contagious.

By the time I reach Ditchling Beacon, some seven hours from London, and look down over the Brighton sea, I have run right out of my grandfather's skin, right out of my own. Nothing contains me; I am the line of my running. Balanced between pain and ecstasy, I pleasure myself by enduring. I have run the north end of Baffin, across New Zealand at Auckland, I have run Hawaii, New York, and Boston, the Niagara Escarpment, the gravelled shores of the Deh Cho and the Mackenzie Delta. What more could I be than this?

Three Inuit carvings: a woman yearning, her face lifted to the wind, an ulu made of baleen in her hand, the tail of her parka swept upward in a pleasing arc by the swirling snow, caught against the background rock descending to a solid base with her feet; a stone hunter, standing poised with a spear, his heavy posture, the massive stone, his character, continuous; another hunter, more visceral in detail, lifting the carcass of a seal toward his face so he can spit fresh water into its mouth and honour its spirit, the seal's lower edges merged with the stone snow at the hunter's feet. I have other carvings, many of whales and one of an aging wrestler, solemnly flexing his stone muscles, and a small ivory whale from New Zealand, a Maori shape that sits warm in the hand, at home among Inuit dreams.

And I have scrimshaw, gifts from my grandfather Austin, gifts from my father, two whale's teeth etched with the pattern of ships by someone who knew rigging and sails so well their lines sing in the wind on the ivory that holds them.

There is a Canadian Government Printing Bureau publication, dated 1906, called *The Cruise of the Neptune: Report on the Dominion Government Expedition to Hudson Bay and the Arctic Islands on Board the DGS* Neptune *1903–04* by A. P. Low, B.Sc., F.R.G.S., in which the edges of photographs are violated with astonishing candour; as, for instance, on page 5 where the lower edge of a photographed icescape becomes painted waves which, in the centre portion, become lines of graphic design which, picture this, near the bottom turn to foreground swirls against the unsuspecting paper. Do you follow: the edges do not

circumscribe. It is a wonderful notion, in a government document!
Ovals of Arctic, exploded rectangles, imploding squares, escaped lines,
errant space. A wondrous notion! Was it Mr. A. P. Low, Fellow of the
Royal Geographic Society, who sanctioned this? Or someone else,
more than a lifetime ago?

In a massive book published in 1885, entitled *Our North Land: Being
a Full Account of the Canadian North-West and Hudson's Bay Route,
Together with a Narrative of the Experiences of the Hudson's Bay Expedition
of 1884, including a Description of the Climate, Resources, and the Characteristics of the Native Inhabitants Between the 50th Parallel and the Arctic
Circle*, Charles R. Tuttle sneaks in the occasional lyric of his own
devising amid the tables and charts and documentary reports. East of
Ungava, in northern Labrador, Tuttle came across an Inuit grave,
"rudely described by the following impromptu lines, pencilled on the
spot." The poem does not bear repeating, but that is not the point.
Sometimes poetry is the only way to breach the apparent inconsequen-
tiality of expositional prose. Later, on the shores of Prince of Wales
Sound, Tuttle came upon an Inuit wedding: he notes in his preamble
to another poem, "there is very little ceremony connected with an
Eskimo marriage, not even with the marriage of a chief's only daugh-
ter, and that little consists of the fortunate man conducting his wife
from the tent of her people to the tent of his people. That is all there
is to it." Tuttle misrepresents Inuit reality, misappropriates their
world; but that is not the point here, either.

Tuttle and Low cannot resist connecting their dissociated sensibilities
as outsiders in the Arctic, through artistic flourishes at the margins of
their texts, with more familiar aesthetics than their Arctic documents
allow. Low's curious expressionism and the pre-Raphaelite posturings
of Tuttle displace the strangeness of an Arctic world perceived as
artifact. Like the stylized illustrations in earlier texts, or imprecations
to God or the Victorian sense of destiny, or like the pandering of so
many writers to their reader's thirst for vicarious suffering, their
intrusions are comforting reminders of the great created world to
which the Arctic is peripheral, a world in which the writer and his

readers share common cultural traditions, common bonds. Far from being divisive, these are points of recognition, which lead the reader on; signposts to reality as metaphor.

Language as text has a way of rendering experience opaque; the limits of opacity are blindness and ignorance. Perception fails in the glare of paper light; vision is circumscribed by meaning. Precision can be evasive; the right word can be wrong.

Barbara Duden in *The Woman Beneath the Skin* disparages contemporary medicalization of pregnancy and the emptiness of language in current women's discourse. Not only are words such as *trimester* and *parturition* dehumanizing, but nonspecific words such as *sexuality*, *sisterhood*, and *empowerment* imply nebulous conditions against which the actual experience of women will inevitably seem wanting. Then what has politically correct language, which is replacing the paternalistic jargon of ethnology and anthropology, done to Inuit reality?

Few women from the outside participated in the early explorations of the Arctic; they were home, as Carol Smith-Rosenburg has documented, writing secret letters. They had stories of their own, but the plot lines were discontinuous, intersecting privately, intimately, and with discretion mistaken for silence. In bureaucratic narratives of the Arctic the design of Inuit lives unravelled, and women's stories seemed like skeins of gossip, circumscribed by silence.

Drowning in 1987; October. Lungs ripped; heart like a bloody fist; eyes imploding and the mucous fragments soaring upward into the receding light. While I was drowning in the deep saltwater off Kailua, I began to compose a letter to my high school gym teachers. It began, Dear Mr. Volpe, Mr. Richardson, and Mr. Mackenzie. Overhead, my place among the throng of swimmers closed and then my body kicked into automatic action against the affront and in furious pain I rose upward into air and breathed; and, battered, swam another two kilometres empty of any awareness but of water and the sky.

Retching bloody fluids cycling out across the hot black lava fields to Hilo and back, I lost the pace but held a steady, slowing rhythm, gulping wind; and picked up my open letter. Dear Sirs, you won't remember me. Well, maybe you will, Mr. Mackenzie, because by grade thirteen I'd filled out a bit and played football, although I didn't know the rules, I really didn't know the rules, but I moved with the action and for one brief season played the game. Mr. Richardson, I remember your eyes. I was the skinny kid with the dark brown hair you used to smile at in knowing confraternity; you must have been through an awkward phase yourself, but mine was lasting forever. After a couple of years with Nick Volpe, I was desperate for acknowledgement, but pity made me wary. Volpe, this is for you. Riding drowning on a bicycle in the Ironman, Hawaii, 1987, I couldn't get the oxygen to feed my quads, but riding standing, using body weight, gear ratio, and gravity, well, damn you, I was making it. I was making it, Nick Volpe, the scrawny hey-you kid was doing the Ironman.

On the run, muscles on the verge of seizure didn't quit. Hour after hour; body, a cerebral mechanism. Hovering between focused concentration and manic contemplation. I lost track of my letter. I wasn't doing it for them. Nick Volpe with his awards for winning teams, coach of all-star athletes, former athlete, after more than thirty years stopped hurting. He couldn't reach me anymore.

Rounding the halfway point, marked by a giant can of Budweiser beer, I run out of the sun into tropical twilight. All the clichés rattle through; do it, make it happen, go the distance. Running on words; running. And then, as the deep night descends, I see a runner moving toward me, a familiar gait. I can feel the taste of my own tears. It's Virginia, coming out to run me in. Sympathy is enervating; she's cool, encouraging. The tears burn my sun-seared skin. I try to speed up in the darkness, to show her I can do it, but I'm drowning still. We move together in a line of runners, moving slowly to the finish. Seventeen hours and change, and then it's done.

I was hospitalized, tubed overnight as a precaution against secondary drowning. We went to the awards banquet the next evening. Sometimes I think of the letter when I'm out there running, but Mr. Volpe, Mr. Richardson, and Mr. Mackenzie are old men now, or dead; no more than emptied metaphors; real people at last. It's all a matter of perspective.

I have not yet read in anthropology or fiction or in the documentary narratives of early contact with the Inuit, written by men, that the trading of wives, from another viewpoint, is the trading of husbands. Diamond Jenness, while judging the intelligence of his subjects by measuring their skulls, acknowledges that among the Inuit the sexes are in most respects equal; even names are gender free. Yet when an Inuit woman he knows exchanges husbands with another woman, so that she can travel a great distance with the other man to visit her family, Jenness ignores her freedom and refers to the habitual sharing of wives. Never does he consider that sexual intercourse might express something other than a territorial prerogative; that notions about possession of the land and genital imperialism are linked.

Language is preemptive. The word *marriage* in English carries with it sacramental connotations of obedience and ownership, according to which the Inuit fall short. If the igloo is described in English as a snow "house," then as a house it is weird, inadequate. A few Victorian writers fancifully described the igloo as if it were an opaque crystal palace in miniature, an English garden folly made of glass. Most described it as an airless hovel; like a lair or den, a fetid cave of snow. But why not, instead of house, which has no meaning to a people for whom the land itself is home, why not the landscape as apparel, or why not ice-clad carapace; not house, but the nearly perfect adaptation of landscape to human needs? Snow houses collapse in spring; replaced by houses made of skin and bones, and layers of ancient growing things and boulders at the edges. So much for houses; or for the house as synecdoche for genealogy or home.

From my grandmother, I have no artifacts.
There are several pieces of furniture I think were hers

which I retrieved when 231 Queen Street was sold;
or had been hers, in trust.
She was always old in my lifetime
but I truly believed she had been young;
there were photographs and anecdotes.
She has not become a story, nor history;
and I have no artifacts to shape my memory,
and I count on dreams;
and I hear the voices of my mother,
the voice of all my mothers
running through my veins.

Destination. It is a word not separable from destiny. The reduction of process to the point of completion, proscriptive linearity is the denial of linear intersection, a garden of forking paths that ultimately lead to the same conclusion. When destination supersedes reality — the journey's end, the journey — then living, even living well, is a dangerous illusion. Think of the Northwest Passage and of all who died there or failed because their objective was more important than their survival. Think of Scott and his dying friends, burdened by rock samples that eventually reached home, although the men perished. Think of Hubbard dying, and then think of Mina Hubbard, for whom the Labrador wilderness offered opportunity to share her husband's last experiences, not a trackless waste through which to channel her ambition. And think of Samuel Hearne, whose book *A Journey to the Northern Ocean* celebrates his connections with the landscape and its people and leaves officials of the Hudson's Bay Company and his readers to draw from his account their own conclusions.

In a book called *"Gossip" A Spoken History of Women of the North*, edited by Mary Crnkovich, women tell of their experience in the Arctic, describe conditions of their lives rather than their destinations, draw meaning from being — rather than the converse. In their many written voices the women of this contemporary book affirm experience over imminence, and place itself as destiny.

Trinh T. Minh-ha, in her evisceration of Claude Lévi-Strauss in *Woman, Nature, Other,* describes anthropology as "gossip," the speaking together about others. It is hard to know when language follows, when language leads.

Nanook of the North. Robert Flaherty's film on Arctic life appeared in 1922. Its black-and-white images, indelible: the smiling-solemn Stone Age hunter; scene upon scene staged for authenticity. In *My Eskimo Friends,* which came out the same year, Flaherty describes his struggle to capture the heroic simplicity of the Arctic people, the primal beauty of their land, in images accessible to imaginations primed for sentimental icons of purity and innocence.

Flaherty created the Inuk his audience expected to see and, although the man called Nanook died of starvation not long after the film was completed, Flaherty's Neolithic caricature thrived as the flickering embodiment of a primeval Arctic for a generation or more, invasive even now as the shallow smiling face on ice cream bars and in refrigerator ads.

The key to creative realism is authenticity — fake that, the rest comes naturally. Consider Yves Thériault's *Agaguk.* It has sold nearly half a million copies since it was first published in 1957. It is standard fare on school curricula, especially in Quebec. It has been celebrated by critics, including myself, both for its allegorical transformation of Inuit life into an emblem of emerging Québécois nationalism and for the apparent accuracy of its vision of Inuit reality. Yet, for all that, it is racist, sexist, and an egregious misappropriation of native experience. *Agaguk* is a well-made piece of fiction and an insensitive sham. In French; and in translation.

In the opening sentence young Agaguk sets out "across the land of the endless tundra, flat and monotonous like the winter sky, without horizon and without trees." Despite the image, it is summer. The perspective is southern; the landscape described in terms of what it lacks. Seasons and directions are measured in terms of the diurnal southern sun. Agaguk and the serenely pliant Iriuk claim "their own acres of ground." This is not only an alien notion, but inimical to the traditional Inuit values the young couple is meant to be reviving. They mate "savagely on the damp and resilient surface of the tundra," and then sleep — apparently immune to flies, mosquitoes, and the terrible abrasions of northern vegetation. Agaguk tells her of people who live in igloos the year round; there are no such people. Agaguk declares of the wind, "It is stronger than I am. Nothing must be stronger than I am." Such an hubristic display reflects southern values, the conventions of Western literature. Thériault's Arctic is a fictional device.

The problem, then, is how to reconcile our appreciation of the novel's inherent aesthetic value with our revulsion at the mendacity of its falsely realistic vision. I'm not sure, but I suspect that the only solution is the evasive and irresponsible notion of art for art's sake, in which case no reconciliation is necessary.

It would be absurd to legislate the imagination. But if misappropriation occurs in the course of writing another's life, if the lines running through the text between writer and reader, between textual reality and actuality, limit or distort that other's world, then such a work should be treated with the same contempt in which we hold the mindless tracts of misogynists, racists, and religious fanatics. When another's world is turned into metaphor, to give meaning to the writer's own, its metamorphosis denies the original of intrinsic worth. Such denial, as in *Agaguk*, is authoritarian aggression more than impropriety. Yet it is, in terms of literature, effective.

The critic Ben-Zion Shek has furiously documented the extent of Thériault's impertinence. He points out that Thériault was director of cultural activities for the Department of Indian and Northern Affairs in the mid-1960s on the basis of appropriated Indian ancestry. Thériault proclaimed himself Montagnais, the apparent authenticity of his fiction proof enough in Ottawa of native blood.

Thériault and his writing won many awards, including the Governor General's, the Molson Prize, and the Prix David. For the art of his expertise on native experience, for making the reality of others unreal.

In Flaherty's book there is a photograph of the man called Nanook; he smiles for the photographer's benefit, tolerant and skeptical, posed as a hunter.
He is standing straight to the camera, framed in phosphorescent light.
He is dead before the photograph
was processed into print.

In the opening section of *The Living Arctic*, Hugh Brody talks of the smiling Eskimo, in stereotypic contradistinction to the cunning Indian. It suited an expanding Western world to envision lands with agricultural potential populated by hostile indigenes, while peoples of the austere Arctic landscape that was in itself of no consequence to alien imperatives readily served as object lessons in cheerful, mindless fortitude. Or as the primal embodiment of adversity. Pejorative metonomy; as in Thériault a clever trope disguised as artifact.

I see myself a hologram suspended in a diorama, crouched in midair among six Polar Eskimos in a Smithsonian display case. The darkness of the corridor behind me thrusts my front-lit reflection into a scene of uproarious laughter, stilled like a photograph of death. The caption reads: "Call THAT a seal?" An explanatory note clarifies: "The whole family enjoys a good laugh at the youth who called out the dog team to haul the undersized seal which he harpooned through a hole in the ice." The dogs especially are well done, while the human figures, although individuated mannequins, lack the benefit of the taxidermist's skill. I am bent to see the boy's expression, but my image hovers through the sloped glass just above his shoulder, between the grinning mother figure who carries a happy infant in her *amautik* and the figure of the laughing father. In other cases displaying Native Cultures of America in the National Museum of Natural History, Smithsonian Institution, Washington, D.C., no one is laughing, although among the Central American Indians a faint smile here and there plays on the mouths of female effigies and small children. A scalp and instruments of war accompany the Woodland Indians display.

believing/you cant get the mind behind glass

George Bowering said that before I did, in a poem despite its title having nothing to do with Mark Trail.

The same A. P. Low, in whose Arctic text the falling away of margins is a liberating achievement, was responsible for the erroneous map of the Labrador interior that led, in part, to the death of Leonidas Hubbard. The Canadian Geological Survey map ascribed to Low was made, apparently, from "hearsay." That is the word used by Dillon Wallace, who survived.

Hubbard misread the subtext of his adventure, the land itself. Imagined maps superimposed on landscape can be lethal, with consequences more immediate perhaps than the murderous aftermath of speculative anthropology or the fiction of apparent authenticity. Hubbard failed to recognize the map as metaphor; he read it literally. Its attenuated lines of continuity, in his mind, extended from the unreliable wilderness to the world outside, map lines connecting consciousness with familiar terrain.

Daphne Marlatt's words in *Ana Historic* (they might have been for Mina Hubbard): she is writing her desire to be,   in the present tense, retrieved from silence . . . each evening she enters her being, nameless, in the book she is writing against her absence. for nothing that surrounds her is absent. far from it.

I think the Hood perhaps is the perfect Arctic river
from the photographs
in which I find myself imagining
in a sort of empirical philology

as we hurtle through the gorges
and stare enraptured at the water's falling
drinking coffee on the cliff tops
in the northern sweep of the Arctic evening's sun
muffled well against the chill
that if I read this landscape openly
I will perhaps become a part of the authentic Arctic text
as if I were a stone figure
or a human being at home.

In pressing to the limit I find
the only form of transcendence I know
that is not also a denial.
You make of landscape what you will
and what you are
until in the beauty of experience
you become what you behold
your life a complement
to the world in contemplation
your presence indivisible
from what you see.

Bending every muscle to the paddle
with Virginia in the bow
in the second day across Algonquin
eighty-five kilometres twenty-two portages
in the sheeting rain whitecaps lashing gunnels
and the sky at midday an obsidian thunderhead
the water galled blue-black
the wind in furious dissonance
I am in love
and bend with every muscle to enduring dreams.

4

ON THE HISTORIOGRAPHICS
OF DESIRE

(I) LANDSCAPE WRITING LANDSCAPE

*S*TART WITH HISTORY. We have made the historical text a secular and restrictive bid for immortality. But landscape is the living presence of our passage; history in the end is history.

It is midnight in Nuuk and Greenland is outside our room in all directions. We are reading aloud from *Ana Historic*, set in Vancouver. It is February now and in Vancouver the flowers are already threatening with spring, but here the Northern Lights play on the window in translucent waves of green and winter scrapes ingenuously against the outer walls. My voice, then Virginia's, shape out the darkened corners of the room with words from worlds away. Neither of us can sleep, although it has been dark for half a day already. We are staying with an ancient family, their Norse and Inuit blood an alliance before history began. If we could see to the west, through the banks of dancing light beyond the open waters of Davis Strait, we would see Canada, Broughton Island, and Baffin.

Within a context defined by consciousness of time, infinity and silence are forms of chaos. These, the written word subjects to the ordering of syntax and narrative design, an intricate continuum extending from paradise to apocalypse.

Listen, he said, listen;
and he spoke of Kittigazuit
where undulations of the low terrain
echo ancient lineage
and only ruins and a few recorded
memories remain;
he spoke of southern Baffin
where the Itijjagiac and Kuujuaq converge,
where circles, broken now,
lie deep against the lichen,
and the valleys and the mountains take the shape
of ancient dreams.
Listen;
and he spoke of Arctic places
as if time were nothing passing
and anything that happened happens still.

But this is nothing, I imagine him saying [this is another voice, this one from *Ana Historic.* this is nothing]. meaning unreadable. because this nothing is a place he doesn't recognize, cut loose from history and its relentless progress towards some end. this is undefined territory, unaccountable. and so on edge.

In Arctic quietude is an absence of language; there is apparently illimitable terrain. Once entered, the only way out again to the world where time is a text is to write yourself into words, to combine exploration with historiography and emerge a literary fact. No wonder so many returned and return to the infinite silence of their Arctic experience, to chaos.

Standing on a rocky point of land near Arctic Bay with my brother on his first trip to the high north, remembering the past as it might have been a thousand years ago when Inuit wintering here could see the same blue hills across Admiralty Inlet, I tried to imagine their lives extensions of my own, but I did not know the words, in Inuktitut, for the water or the land. I can only see in English, and as Richard reminisced about the Dorset and the Thule cultures who left behind the boulder rings in slow decay around us, and in the distance the town site spread awkwardly against the sloping rubble rising from the shore, I thought of all the deaths that passed between me now and those other human beings, who lived here in another language on the other side of history, and I felt the emptiness between us, between the landscape inseparable from their consciousness of being alive and the inchoate text from which I peered out at the remnants of their world.

Ask what is history, how is history made? How does it relate to time, to consciousness and individual experience, to place? Where is the landscape in history, and what is the text, the historiographic moment, in the reality of landscape? If I read George Back's *Narrative of the Arctic Land Expedition*, which describes his travels in the northern Barrens, in the original 1836 edition that now sells for $600 in Kingston, or if we take the same amount of money to outfit ourselves for a two-week trek across the Itijjagiac plateau of southern Baffin, and we write of our adventures, and read books along the way, which will lead to better understanding Arctic history and history itself, to a more thoughtful appreciation of Arctic narrative, of time and the Arctic landscape? What if we took Back's leather-bound *Narrative* with us instead of *Howards End* or Stephen Hawking's paperback encounter with the universe? What if there were no books, just memories and dreams?

Whatever else history is text.
Where there is no story there is only story.
What is written into empty landscape
is the only landscape there is.

Historiography is not a mnemonic device. It is the dispositioning of mind by text, a denial of the human in the transformation of time and space into printed artifact.
Nature in history is a printscape; natural religion, obsolete; and native peoples, an obtrusive anomaly.
The historical text has meaning only in relation to other texts.

The Inuit who first met Europeans in the pursuit of history were instructed on being remote, at the edges of meaning. Their place in the world was empty: their landscape had yet to be written. But to locate oneself on a map or in writing acknowledges the separation of consciousness from the object of its contemplation. Amid the proliferation of Arctic narratives the Inuit became words (and now read of themselves in the desire of others) and, elliptically, become real (strangers in their own place sometimes even to themselves).

On the north end of Baffin Island, while I thought about naming as the tactical spearhead of historical invasion, while I heard deep inside the voices dying of a hundred generations, and I scanned the landscape, taking in the blue-grey hills mounded like a Neolithic bestiary, taking in my grown daughters leaping shore ice with their friends, their laughter arcing among the boulder circles, bowhead vertebrae, and fallen roofs, taking in Virginia's exploration of wildflowers among the greening bones, I listened also to Richard in a raptured frenzy cross-referencing expectations and experience, talking of ships and whaling, explorers, disasters, and books as lichen that had endured centuries crumbled under our weight.

There is an iceberg among the aging books scattered on the floor around me while I write in Bellrock, surrounded by Arctic artifacts, immersed in Arctic memories; an iceberg I will write about, as I write about these old books with their marbled covers, and insinuate my words into the voluminous library of Arctic narrative; an iceberg that lies sandwiched flat between seraphic paragraphs, etched on browning paper; a documentary iceberg, Gothic, allusive, which will become in my own text like a crumbling palisade, an elephant, a flaming tower in the golden sun.

Outsiders have transformed the Arctic into photographs, engravings, the profligate word. Every venture into Arctic landscape, recorded to extend knowledge of the known world and impose meaning on the unknown, participates in a text of infinite complexity. From the fabulous accounts of Pythias to frenetic press releases by the beleaguered Weber-Malakhov Expedition of 1992, Arctic narrative has displaced actuality in the search to connect with other narratives, as each encounter with the Arctic enters an extensive verbal construct, the reality of print. Measured and named, the landscape has become geography; written into narrative, it is history.

We are caught between geography and history in Canada, between naming and story. Exploration has taken the place of significant event and we yearn to venerate surveyors and cartographers, Hearne and Mackenzie, Franklin, Thompson, Fraser, writers all, and foreigners. We name the landscape for them, as they, for us. We are a nation in writing, perennially rewriting ourselves.

Monday, July 20, 1992. In brief coronas of the Arctic cottons' sheen, before the sun recedes, and in the rake of boulders rising into luminescent clouds, cloud shadows; in the soothing tremulations of the water-laden wind, the chiaroscuro flash of a bunting's rapid turn; in the peregrine's held flight and the raven's garbled cry — is every element of our beginning and imagery anticipating history at the journey's end.

It is difficult from the promiscuous photograph of Sir John Franklin, embedded in the pages of dozens of accounts of Arctic exploits, to comprehend the desires that led him to undertake his final expedition. Although the daguerreotype is soiled, the pose stilted, the visage calculated to convey dignity and accomplishment, there is a look of childlike terror in the old man's eyes. After a career as the governor of Tasmania, in consequence of his early exploits, which were documented with classic understatement in books popular in his day, journals relating in meticulous detail a survey of the western Arctic, periodically interspersed with accounts of hardship and treachery, starvation, mutiny, cannibalism, and murder, he chose to sail the Northwest Passage not, apparently, because of an absence in his life, but simply because he could not resist returning to the centre of the Arctic story. The horror is in the photograph; in illusions of actuality and the story's end.

Franklin's last photograph begins the modern era of Arctic exploration.

Walking with Virginia across the Meta Incognita Peninsula, named on a whim by the first Queen Elizabeth, I see in the brilliant air a landscape tumultuous with dreams. Baffin is the image of time; the convergence in every footstep over rock and tundra, among the efflorescent splendour of Arctic flowers, of the world and desire. That's how it seems as we labour beneath our heavy packs into the Kuujuaq Valley, coming off the Itijjagiaq, traditional Inuit routes for the annual summer gathering at a lake called Amadjuaq. All of this will be named next week: Katannilik, meaning the place of the falls, dedicated as a territorial park. The Kuujuaq will be declared, after several thousand years of travel, a heritage river. History takes time.

Walking with Virginia toward Lake Harbour, when I'm walking in the lead I sometimes lose myself in what I see; sensory experience and the landscape seemingly the same.

This is not about recovery of place
or appropriations of a misplaced past;
this is not about history as archaeology
nor about the archaeology of dreams —
it is about landscape, language, and time,
about entering the story that is there before you,
the enveloping text, simultaneously
continuous and discontinuous from one volume to another,
along shelves, among corridors
that reach through cavernous chambers
throughout a library that opens,
Borgesian, into other libraries —
like ordered chaos in explosive clusters on a hard drive;
it is about consciousness and the death of time.

Imagine a pair of cashmere gloves lying palm upward on a rock. They are in the High Arctic, on Beechey Island, and they have been exposed to four successive winters, stones placed carefully in each palm, holding them in place. The fingers rise in the sunlight to cradle the stones, the offprint of their shape darkening the greyed lichen in shadows flecked with filaments of wool. Annually the gloves clench and relax, rise to the sun and fall back against the frozen surface of the rock, and rise and fall again until someone picks them up as an artifact, leaving only a slight discoloured blur on the lichen, on the rock you are imagining.

August 29, 1850. Ten vessels in all are gathered at Beechey Island north of Baffin, in the breaking ice off Barrow Strait. It is only two days after the discovery of the Franklin Expedition's first winter encampment, where three graves were found, neatly engineered within the permafrost, including one whose stonework mound is in the country fashion, less a memorial than the others, the burial place of twenty-year-old stoker John Torrington, whose frozen corpse will eventually be excavated, thawed with careful applications of hot water, and photographed for world distribution, featured on the cover of a book by the forensic pathologist who disinterred him and reconstituted into Gothic images by Margaret Atwood in *Wilderness Tips*.

The convergence of ten vessels at Beechey on a single day may seem improbable when you consider that in the preceding 354 years only 122 voyages by outsiders had been made into Arctic waters (since Sebastian Cabot crossed the Arctic Circle under letters patent from King Henry VIII).

August 29, 1850. Ten vessels. British and American. From the public purse and private enterprise; for the humane necessity of resolving the unknown; for science. All in search of Franklin; each with a full complement of writers — listen, you can hear the scratching pens, the drying of ink, locks clicking in the secret places where journals, field notes, sketchbooks, diaries, logs, histories, memoirs, narrative reports, poems, and stockpiled letters are being guarded and nurtured among rare shadows thrown by a nighttime Arctic sun. The typological and intertextual implications reverberate through libraries, among histories, and in the minds of scholars and poets, in the perceptions of travellers, the sensibility of every outsider who holds the Arctic land-scape an optional reality in imagination, and among the bibliographies of Arctic dreaming.

July 1992. Baffin. I have brought with me Hawking's *A Brief History of Time*. Aritha van Herk, after much deliberation, determined Tolstoy's *Anna Karenina* the ideal book for backpacking in the interior of Ellesmere. She later wrote about herself and Anna, about Tolstoy and islands, about the convergence of history, literature, and experience in the High Arctic, in a book she describes with awkward precision as *geografictione*. Hawking's book seems more appropriate on Baffin, to keep everything imagined in perspective. Here the desolation is illusion, and the awesome, fragile beauties of the season absolute. For balance I picked up *Howards End* in the Northern Store in Iqaluit; rescuing E. M. Forster from the vampires and violence, his overween-ing Englishness a pleasing foil, in our nightly readings, to the pleasant emptiness of muscular exhaustion.

It is late evening and the sun is low in the north; the sky gathers around us in the long shadows of the Kuujuaq Valley and opens high over-head. Virginia is asleep in the tent, and I am hunkered on my side around the small camp stove, keeping watch as fresh bannock slowly turns to amber, my fetal posture protecting the delicate flame from a gentle ground breeze. My cup is empty, but I hold it close beneath my nose to catch the residual pungency of the botrytised riesling we drank earlier to celebrate the day; a half bottle packed in among the freeze-dried meals; the sun-bruised grapes a carnival in the summer Arctic air.

Had Franklin or his men survived, had the *Erebus* and *Terror* endured, library shelves would gape and the Arctic landscape, fully surveyed, would be a different geography, with different names, a different history. As it was, publishers could not keep up with the frenzy over Franklin's wondrous demise; time and again the editors or ghostwrit-ers, in prefaces to accounts of the search, acknowledge their principal authors' departure on fresh expeditions before the final texts were bound and delivered. The beauty of disaster, when only a scattering of its details are known, is the infinite elasticity by which it absorbs new forays into what has become essentially a fiction.

February 1993. Greenland. We are reading aloud, enclosed in this small borrowed room, sheltered from an Arctic that is strange to us. This is winter, and we are summer familiars. Daphne Marlatt's haunting words, silences broken by memories of the body, of language, of imagination, connect us to a world more known. This is not like Norway, where we travelled as far north as you can go in Europe, in August of 1991, to Kirkenes on the Barents Sea. This is not like Iceland, where in 1976 I spent a few long chilly days in late September before flying on to a conference on Canada in Normandy. For all its Western demeanour, its European connections, this is an Inuit place. The landscape outside these walls is not a language I understand. In the Canadian Arctic I read the landscape in English, if only in translation. Here history is Scandinavian and the landscape, in translation, Danish.

> Soon after rounding Point Warren (named . . . after my friend Captain Samuel Warren, of the Royal Navy), we crossed the mouth of a large river, the water being muddy and fresh for the breadth of three miles, and the sounding lead was let down to the depth of five fathoms, without striking the bottom. This river is, perhaps, a branch of the Mackenzie, and falls into a bay, on which I have bestowed the name of my esteemed friend Copland Hutchison, Esq., Surgeon Extraordinary to His Royal Highness the Duke of Clarence. On its east side there is an island, which was named after Captain Charles Phillips, of the Royal Navy, to whom the nautical world is indebted for the double-capstan, and many other important inventions.

The natives of this place, according to Dr. John Richardson's account, "called themselves Kitti-garroe-oot, (inhabitants of the land near the mountains)." Undulations of the low terrain echo ancient lineage; only ruins and a few recorded memories remain. Three graves crown the summit of a hill at Kittigazuit, surrounded by improbable rectangles of picket fencing, Inuit names in English carved into silvered headboards. Between Richardson, on the second Franklin expedition, passing by in July of 1826, and Virginia and me in the summer of 1989, 163 years later, warming ourselves in the lee of a low stone wall curved against the earth, the histories of exploration, whaling, settlement, influenza, and abandonment crowded like pedestrians at a stoplight on an empty thoroughfare.

Today I heard Greg Curnoe died.

That painful sentence stands in isolation. I have a bicycle drawn by Greg, framed between sheets of Plexiglas held together with binding screws exactly as he prescribed in a letter taped to the back. It is a side-view pen sketch of a 21″ track frame built by Doc Morton around 1935, ridden by Charles Viaene of Strathroy & Delhi in the early 40s. The drawing is dated nov. 3/1973. Greg's signature is stamped from an inkpad in the top right-hand corner. He was killed in a bicycle accident; today is nov. 16.

Greg introduced himself over the phone in the spring of 1961 and invited me to his studio. I was graduating from Western, or thought I was, and all that held me back from England and a Kensington garret was money. Through his huge moustache Greg talked of London, London on the Ontario Thames; before long I was talking Waterloo County. We spent an afternoon celebrating sou-west-o. I didn't risk going back. After summer school, I went abroad, let my hair grow, lived in a garret, and typed out poems and stories about Waterloo County and London, Ont.

The visionary enthusiasm of Greg Curnoe's art and life sanctioned my reality, made it possible. The past is personal; real history is how we know its presence. Greg in mind was like my grandmother, who grew up near London, in Granton, and at a century old remained ecstatic in her passion for the particulars of who we are.

1944. Victoriaville, Quebec. The wet and brittle sound of early
      spring.
Maple syrup mist and spiralled woodsmoke merging overhead;
damp wool, grey trees, the smell of horses.
My father in his storm-blue trench coat, my mother
in lamb's fur with a muskrat collar.
My father in huge flight boots, the zippers open
so they flare impressively; my mother, wearing
elegant galoshes, black with heels.
My brother in breeches and stiff leather boots, high-cuts.
I must be wearing breeks, too,
or woolen leggings; and a fighter pilot bonnet.

Trudging over snow; my mother's voice,
behind me, pliant.
My only French, *bonjour.*
Merci. Fermez la bouche.
This, too, is part of the war effort.

We pose for a photograph with our host,
the officer in charge; I'm not in it.
I must be somewhere
licking maple taffy from the snow:
or frozen horse piss, my brother's inspiration.
He is in the shadows of the picture,
beside Esmond Romily, my father's friend,
shot down off Singapore in '45.

In early June of 1992 we fly into Lake Dumoine with Julia and George
and paddle the spring rush downriver to the Ottawa. The water is
different from last August; swollen with the spring runoff and more
ambiguous to read. Flying in, we can see it follows the same course,
but riding it down, the rocks and water, even the shoreline present
different contours, a different text. Nor is it the same landscape from
the air and by canoe, although our maps and common sense insist on
areal coincidence. Had we been backpacking along the river's tangled

banks, it would be another place. Or were we voyageurs with other imperatives and, certainly, other desires, it would seem a different order of experience. We talk about the voyageurs, how most died by thirty, about Jean Baptiste Le Moyne, who in 1697, at seventeen, paddled upriver with a party of soldiers to confront the English at Hudson Bay, and about the Hurons, who to avoid an Iroquois toll on their way to Quebec detoured around the Ottawa on this same river. The same place; different worlds.

Walk through library stacks among the bound journals of Arctic arcana, scientific reports in thick, perfect binding, books shouldering books in shelf upon shelf; here and there you encounter, in those splendid acts of serendipity reserved for lovers of print, tomes that smell of leather and dust and senescent paper, not chemicals and antiseptic glue. Names in gold impressed across the desiccating spines of one cluster in particular ring with history: M'Clure, M'Clintock, Kane, Hall. Weigh each volume carefully in turn and open to the title page — and whatever the title, the subtitle, anticipating the subtext of each adventure, reads in variants of Hall's *Life with the Esquimaux*, "A Narrative of Arctic Experience in Search of Sir John Franklin's Expedition."

Seated in the stacks on one of those little awkward stools with the retractable wheels, you move casually through the rough-cut pages, edges softened by stale air, the paper brightening inside toward centres that have rarely seen light, perhaps never fluorescence, the print fresh black after a century and a half, and Franklin is there in the subtext, among the most wonderful woodcuts and etchings that southern engravers could make from the words of explorers, their field notes and anecdotes and ghostwritten memoirs; and the fate of Franklin's men is acknowledged as much in the beauty as the raw, brutal imagery of utterly alien terrain, the beauty lending grace, and the brutality, heroics to their assured but unknown demise.

No one writes about flowers by Torrington's grave
Wind and snow and desolation reticulate on paper
the imagery of death

There is campion on Beechey saxifrage
and the flare of Arctic poppy flecks of purple
brilliance ochre but the wheeling sky
articulates despair

Summer grasses
evade metaphor

Death amid woodcuts the words the imagery inscribed
on barren landscape dead
Absent flowers the nexus of a thousand stories
reiterate despair

On page 105 of the popular narrative of Hall's first Arctic expedition, a page trimmed short for some unknown reason at the bindery, there is a chart affixed with a facsimile seal of authenticity: Esquimaux Chart, No. 1, Drawn by Koojesse at Rescue Harbor, 1860 for C. F. Hall. This remarkable document, reduced for publication to one-twelfth its actual size, describes closure in meticulous lines to Frobisher Strait, and connects the Meta Incognita with the rest of Baffin. What Hall now accepted as Frobisher Bay, Koojesse called Tin-Nu-Jok-Ping-Oo-Se-Ong and drew Hall's hand across the chart, literally outlining the terrain in fine movements of their joined fingers until Hall was convinced the Northwest Passage lay elsewhere, and from Rescue Bay pursued Franklin farther north.

Franklin's orders would have taken him around the top of Baffin and south again to points due west of Hall's position. Captain George Tyson, who sailed as assistant navigator with Hall on his ill-fated third voyage, pointed out with vehemence in *Tyson's Arctic Experience* that the last place anyone looked for Franklin was where he was supposed to be.

I am fifty-two and running; the woods aslant
surround the trail with autumn; the Gatineau
anticipating snow reveals hillsides and ravines

disguised by summer foliage in green. I am
running banks of orange and blue, running
from a high vantage down toward the river
when I hear, I do not imagine this, I hear the sounds
of a steam locomotive, the familiar strange
plaintive haunting rising falling
dying wail, and descending closer I can hear
the chuffing of the engine, I do not imagine it,
the thick slow chuffing of the engine, and then
the rhythmic click of tracks and rolling wheels
I think I see through the trees below
the tops of something moving; when I get to the tracks
beside the river they are rusting but I can hear the train
and I put my ear to the steel the way we did prophetically
as kids. I start running along the tracks toward the sounds
receding upriver, toward Wakefield, like a Colville painting,
running until I can't hear it anymore; then finally I cut upward
into the hills, remembering, remembering my dead Uncle
who took us on the last train from Preston to Hespeler
and told me to remember this because someday I would be
his age, which I am now, and he cried, as if that explained
everything, and I held his hand and cried, too, for the love
of trains, steam engines, time unrecognized until it's passed;
and I could taste the warm salt tears while running home.

I want to add, this is not what I meant to write, running
in the Gatineau; I intended turning Richard Weber,
whose house is close above, into metaphor.
He is, today, in Moscow along with Misha Malakhov
receiving a medal if they're lucky from Boris Yeltsin
for being the first to carry the old-new Russian flag
to the North Pole; last year; nearly.
Perhaps I would extrude from this a discourse
on Arctic books, on history, running, and desire;
running in the Gatineau, I would pattern words, scheme stories,
review narratives into which I would cut my own words,

like etchings, icebergs in a text;
instead, for a few minutes I became a small boy
holding my eccentric Uncle's aging hand,
crying because everything was passing
and we were on the last train
which I heard again today running in the Gatineau.

In almost any Arctic narrative published before the proliferation of photography, you will find a scattering of woodcuts and etchings, sketches and paintings (refined and engraved in the print studios of London, New York, Edinburgh). If you look carefully in the illustrations, your perspective becomes paramount; you can see yourself within the lines and planes and textures of Arctic history.

Here is one by Frederick Beechey, published in 1821: "Iceberg in Baffin's Bay." It is an icing sugar mountain melting from the bottom up, lit from the foreground, even though sunlight against the clouds is from high and to the left. And here is another iceberg, by George Back, a watercolour from the 1830s; the light again is split — this time the contours of frozen light in the foreground thrust crenellated planes almost off the page, while the sunlight itself is from the right, and the entire world to the left is cast in shadow.

Here is an iceberg, between banks of seraphic print, no larger than a dollar, with spires and buttresses, shadowy ledges and efflorescent rubble, identified in the text as a ruined castle, an elephant among broken mountains, a lighthouse bathed in golden fire; it looms within the story by Charles Francis Hall as a Gothic spectral thing — narrative emotion captured, shared, affirmed.

Here is an engraving by Sartain, from a drawing by J. Hamilton of a sketch by Dr. Elisha Kent Kane, of the graves at Beechey beneath soaring, dismal cliffs, highlighted to the brilliance of white paper in a narrow slash behind three Gothic headboards. And here another: the landscape an austere and curiously benign background against which a throng of treacherous Inuit meet the ferocity of British seamen as they attack Captain Franklin's boats not far from Kittigazuit on the Beaufort Sea. The picture, one of a sequence drawn by Captain Back detailing the entire skirmish, is continuous with Franklin's printed text, as authentic in your mind as the written narrative it echoes.

Images converge: lines connect; lines separate, divide. When you enter Arctic narrative, you enter every narrative of the Arctic ever written. When you enter the Arctic in person, you become part of the extended text. When you write the Arctic to affirm your presence in the world, you become in writing an imaginative creation. You could imagine anything and write it down and it would seem real forever.

In Polar adventuring and record-seeking exploits, imperatives and desire merge as complementary attitudes of personal ambition. Exploration of the Arctic had generally been driven by the imperatives of commerce, politics, or ideology. In the narratives of expeditions undertaken for the Royal Navy, the Hudson's Bay Company, *National Geographic*, Parliament, or Congress, the interests being served are usually self-evident. But every account of the Arctic is also informed by the personal and often confusing desires of each writer to shape history from geography, to attain knowledge or wealth, to escape or discover himself, to be famous. The Arctic as a projection of personality is an extension of distant traditions, expression of alien dreams.

On August 27, 1850, a pair of cashmere gloves "with two small stones upon the palms to keep them from blowing away" were found amid the remnants of Franklin's last-known winter camp. Such are the inexpressibly touching details of abandoned landscape included in Dr. Elisha Kent Kane's account of the Beechey site, written, he says, from a journal he kept at the request of his brother to furnish topics for fireside conversation. The official report issued from this particular expedition, under the command of Lieutenant Edwin De Haven of the U.S. brig *Advance*, says nothing of the gloves but notes the stability and order conveyed by the neatness of the graves.

Fame is not the only engine of Arctic exploration, nor the fear of death. To be known by people never met; to extend life even for a paragraph or passing mention in the annals of adventure; to taunt mortality, affect indifference at the edge of annihilation; to drive the self like a stake through the heart of time; to be history — these have much to do with Arctic travel. The yawning gape of gravity that threatens all of us leads some to Arctic landscape, some to write of being there. Some settle comfortably to earth while others, their wings on fire, soar.

In Appendix III of M'Clintock's account, *The Voyage of the 'Fox' in the Arctic Seas: A Narrative of the Discovery of the Fate of Sir John Franklin and His Companions*, there are six pages in fine print listing relics retrieved from the Franklin expedition. One brief paragraph describes a skeleton found nine miles eastward of Cape Herschel in May of 1859. The remains, not identified, are wearing, as a tie, a "black silk necker-chief":

> fragments of a double-breasted blue cloth waistcoat, with covered silk buttons, and edged with braid; a scrap of coloured cotton shirt, silk covered buttons of blue cloth great-coat; [and carrying] a small clothes-brush, a horn pocket-comb, a leathern pocket-book, which fell to pieces when thawed and dried; it contained 9 or 10 letters, a few leaves apparently blank; a sixpence, dated 1831; and a half-sovereign, dated 1844.

The bones are wearing, in the present tense, retrieved from silence, fragments; personality without a name remains obscured.

Our notion of historical time has been somewhat adumbrated by the general theory of relativity, but we still think of time as linear, more elastic perhaps, but still a two-dimensional sequence of separate moments. In the historical model of time we are always at the paper's outer edge as the pages flip between the past and future, a dot on a sequence of edges, the surface illusion of a line in motion.

My dad talked all his life about Hud Stewart,
the rafts they built where the Speed meets the Grand
and the arrowheads they found, the cars
they drove at fourteen into snowbanks.
Hud Stewart was more real than my own childhood,
my rafts evoking stories of historical adventure
and the sunshine days of more exciting summers.
He introduced himself, a shy old man, by my father's casket
in the empty church, the three of us alone, and left
before the service and the obsequies began.

Two ways that history can mean, can have meaning, are through
narrative projection of the present upon the past and a projection
of the narrative past upon the present. In the latter, history comes
of discovering in what has happened some coherent order through
which to explain our perspective on it. We read ourselves into
history in a quest for our own inevitability. Occasionally we are
aware of living in history, when one particular narrative seems
destined to dominate, and we carefully note where we are at the
lasting moment. In the former we write ourselves into history, draw
from heritage and historical imperatives the shape of our present
experience, which we record to affirm the continuity of our being.
The activities of living and of writing are symbiotic as an exercise
in existential progenesis. History is revisionist as we read ourselves
into it (endlessly reworking the infinite versions of a finite text), or
it is visionary — as we choose refuge in the furnaces of historiography and desire (perennially consumed, renewed again and again and
again), and write ourselves into the perpetual presence of a living
text.

You cannot participate in history simply by reading, or by writing and
rewriting the past. Any moment in your life is more complex than all
the convolutions of historical narrative. But you can write yourself into
the present; as an explorer you can document your passing. The
danger, of course, is in believing your own account, confusing your
own vision of the world with the world itself.

In his doctoral dissertation on perceptions of place in the Thelon, James Raffan argues for the natural world as teacher, exploring the question, "how does land impose meaning on human consciousness?" And concludes: it is in part a numinous procedure. He opens with a New Age solipsism by Annie Dillard, from an interview with *Life:*

> According to the second law of thermodynamics, things fall apart. Structures disintegrate. Buckminster Fuller hinted at the reason we are here: By creating things, by thinking up new structures, we counteract this flow entropy. We make new structures, new wholeness, so the universe comes out even. A shepherd on a hilltop who looks at a mess of stars and thinks, "There's a hunter, a plow, a fish," is making mental connections that have as much real force in the universe as the very fires in those distant stars themselves.

That's one way of seeing things. I want to say, not only hint but say, that's a way of seeing things. That's a way of seeing things.

Photographs, illusions of the death of time, separate readers from the text. Although less than colour, even black-and-whites, wet-plate prints, daguerreotypes intrude, or may enhance a text, but do not participate in the narrative itself. M'Clintock describes the ship's doctor aboard the *Fox* in March of 1858, while in pursuit of Franklin's fate, thirteen years after the *Terror* and *Erebus* sailed out of London, as taking a photograph from the ice by the albumen process on glass, the temperature being well below zero at the time.

You cannot photograph history. / This is a poem about history, / about photography and imagination. / You cannot photograph this poem.

In the list of subscribers to the *Fox* expedition appended to M'Clintock's *Narrative*, W. J. C. Bath, Esq., is credited with a donation of two shillings, sixpence; the children of Mrs. Armstrong donated eight shillings, ninepence; the servants of Ashhurst Majendie, Esq., are credited with an offering of fourteen shillings; while "the brother and sisters of the late John and Thomas Hartnell, of H.M.S. 'Erebus,' buried at Beechey Island," are down for five pounds. M'Clintock's book in excellent condition is listed in Kingston at $475; a friend of mine owns a copy, the spine in original leather, although the cover boards are new; it bears the signature on the flyleaf of his great-great grandfather, who sailed with William Parry north of Spitzbergen, and in August of 1827 was one of twelve men to man-haul James Clark Ross's sledge almost to the Eighty-third Parallel.

According to E. Vale Blake's "A General Arctic Chronology," included with his history of the *Polaris* Expedition, published in 1874 by Harper and Brothers of New York and inscribed by hand on the title page, in my copy, volume 532 of the Canadian Library of Parliament Collection (I hold the pages to my nose to get the smell of the fire of 1916), there were 257 volumes published before the curiously arbitrary date of 1857 on Arctic research, "to which may now be added [he wrote with syntactical licence] a host of American, English, and other foreign writers, with a long list of scientific and popular works germane to Polar matters."

The Canadian Heritage Rivers System, under the authority of the Crown, exists for the recognition and preservation of rivers of outstanding significance, in history, natural endowment, and recreational merit. The nomination document for the Soper River, known in Inuktitut as Kuujuaq, gives thirty-two lines to Dewey Soper, most of them under the subheading "of human heritage value" and some under "of Canadian significance." Soper spent the winter, spring, and early summer of 1931 in Lake Harbour, a scientist in government employ. He surveyed the river valley to sixty-three degrees, fifteen minutes north, "as far as the height of navigation," noting especially the profligate breeding of willows (although he did not say it that way), and the luxuriant proliferation of wildflowers.

Evidence of native habitation is acknowledged to extend through four to six millennia. The Inuit, who name the landscape sparingly and in words descriptive of their experience there or for its salient features, have little history. The landscape is who they are. The obscurity of their archaeological and anthropological presence becomes a tantalizing postcolonial subtext in a nomination document that celebrates the area's natural heritage.

Virginia and I carry blank books in our packs, wrapped carefully against the rain and sweat, and each evening in the midnight sun we write to capture words, and usually we read to each other what we have written, to compare. She has prepared her book with pasted fragments from other journals, information about the terrain, maps, and empty spaces. She writes carefully, in blocks of time, into the emptiness and mounts pressed flowers within the waiting text, covering them with clear plastic cut precisely to size. I write a poem or poetic paragraph each day, sometimes spontaneously and sometimes reworking assiduously the coalition of passion and thought that I've been carrying through the heavy hours.

When landscape and language converge in consciousness, sometimes it is necessary to express yourself in poetry; not because poetry has metaphysical potential unavailable to prose but simply because, in acknowledging its own presence on the page, the written poem more honestly admits the text as mediator between experience of the world and the world itself. The same could be said of oral poetry or song, that they shape the air.

I take field notes like dictation from the landscape. One of my notes directs me to reread Dr. John Richardson's diaries of the first Franklin expedition and in particular his report on events from October 10, 1821, to October 23. I can remember the dates. I remember the events. There is little of the Barrens in his account. He describes murder, cannibalism, the hacking of frozen human bodies, fear and madness, the murder of Robert Hood, his summary execution of the murderer, the extremities of cold. Sometimes his prose is visceral in its precision, especially in comparison with Lieutenant Franklin's. But I have no sense of the terrain from his writing, except as impinging conditions.

It would be easy, when the going is tough, to write the landscape into emptiness and fill the vacuum with sensate conditions, visceral responses — the cold, the exhaustion, the fear. I make a note to avoid considering the landscape either an extension of my own adventure or an intrusion on my body's function, the deliberations of survival in difficult circumstances.

but once history's onstage [this is from *Ana Historic*], histrionic as usual (all those wars, all those historic judgements), the a-historic hasn't a speaking part. what's imagination next to the weight of the (f)actual?

Think of a nighttime sky; everything you see is in the past. Standing on a rocky bluff with the town of Nuuk and the harbour spread out before me in subtle tones of darkness and dazzling flecks and spheres and waves of light, everything I see has already happened. I am still and the light that surges through the night and penetrates my vision, some of it is older than the rock beneath my feet, some of it from distant galaxies that died before the Earth began. Spontaneous constellations arrange themselves in mind as I project myself across the universe and, equidistant, patterns form among the buildings lit by incandescent particles that are only milliseconds old and draw me into the community of their design. The harbour and the ghostly landscape holding it in place, they reach my eyes as spectral emanations of a solid world that anticipate and reflect my presence. After a while I am cold and descend into the warmth of hospitality in the town below.

Chapter 32 in volume 1 of Kane's *Arctic Explorations: The Second Grinnell Expedition in Search of Sir John Franklin* is bound upside down in my copy; an aberration, a break in narrative design. The foldout map in volume 1 shows upper Ellesmere as Grinnell Land, and the northwestern edge of Greenland is called Washington. Blank space dominates; small glyphs are listed in a legend to mark uninhabited huts, auks, eider ducks, and walrus sighted; on the map there are no corresponding markers.

Kane's orders from the American secretary of the navy were, on November 27, 1852, to accommodate Lady Franklin by searching for her husband; and on February 9, 1853, to pursue scientific inquiry, particularly "such as relate to the existence of an open Polar sea, terrestrial magnetism, general meteorology, and subjects of importance in connection with natural history." His own inclination, based on experience as ship's doctor on the First Grinnell Expedition, which had taken him to Beechey, was to drive north toward the pole. Franklin was dead; Grinnell, a wealthy New York merchant, was becoming Arctic geography; and Kane, while acquiring fame as a writer, had done nothing to force closure on the Franklin story, nor inscribe his own name on the landscape. His third expedition, ending in disaster, assured the apotheosis he so eloquently courted. And the rest is history.

(II) KATANNILIK JOURNALS

Monday, July 20, 1992.

In brief coronas of the Arctic cottons' sheen,
before the sun recedes,
and in the rake of boulders rising
into luminescent clouds, cloud shadows;
in the soothing tremulations of the water-laden wind,
the chiaroscuro flash of a bunting's rapid turn,
in the peregrine's held flight
and the raven's strangled cry —
is every element of our beginning
and imagery anticipating history
at the journey's end.

Tuesday, July 21, 1992.

For the second day the rain descends in frozen granules
like fine gravel peppering the impermeable ochre surface

of the tent; only where the catch water rises,
sliding over permafrost through mossy clumps beneath
the floor, does moisture enter, evanescent dampness,
while the air outside, opaque, is drenched.
Ginny in the tent is attending to her journal.
Hunched in my Gore-Tex against a rock
I work to heat the tea, the stove beneath a pack cover
stretched between boulders, rain splattering my Stetson,
making it old and handsome. We are pressed by the lowering sky
against the earth, bones folded into muscle, waiting.
Ginny in the tent is a study, perhaps,
in historiographics and desire.
Only yesterday we came by helicopter
across Koojesse Inlet from Iqaluit,
flying over the ice-jammed breakup of Frobisher Bay
(last year we spent thirty hours on the breaking ice
with Laura and Fred, Pauloosie and Jacobee,
to reach Auyuittuq, on the other side of Baffin),
fourteen minutes in the air; jet-powered;
the pilot, Randy, dashing, of course.
And then we were alone and the cold descended
and the rain closed around us
and we were two full weeks away
in a bone-chilling dream
from wakening.
Ginny in the tent is a study
in historiographics and desire.
Stiffened fingers move with surprising agility
across the paper; she is hunched in a deliberate posture,
wearing everything against the cold;
she turns the pages, cuts, lays out her text, sets
flowers pressed against the page with Mac-Tac,
blows tea steam against her fingers, writes
in the spaces she has set herself between the blocks
of research, already mounted; Katannilik, a journal,

with maps, objectives sited in pen,
and whiteout in her kit to cover errors; and scissors; an illustrated
    narrative
summoning completion, as we sit the weather out,
on our second day.
Tomorrow in the rain clouds we'll proceed,
carefully with compass, reading topography. There is time ahead;
    words
to be found, flowers, collected, spaces to fill.
And Ginny in the tent is a study
in historiographics and desire.

Wednesday, July 22, 1992.

Busy in the awkward chill of morning
I forget how old I am, forget my name, forget to watch
my hands, nimble with details, glistening;
I forget everything
but how to eat for the weather, break camp
in the fine mizzle that covers our gear,
how to shoulder the weight, walk out of the circle,
with no evidence left of our passing,
into the opening landscape.

Thursday, July 23, 1992.

Camped on the wrong shore of the Rumbling River,
through a ragged windless night
of freezing rain,
the river's clamour flooding thunder,
dreaming in the raucous dark
of tomorrow's crossing —

you contemplate the river, mind arched
like a raptor riding on the rise of weathered air;
and the white sky lifts to sunlight,

a silver disk, no shadows yet,
and the land's edge looms;
you rehearse the icy water rushing, rock, and sliding depths,
strip boots and pants, don neoprenes,
free up pack straps, adjust your hat,
test your pole again against dry rock,
and cut the waters like a struck char
on a lethal fibrillating line.

Ginny on the Rumbling River is amazing:
far out in the wide expanse
of foaming and converging waters,
between a rugged boulder shore and serrated ice
across the blue/black/green and swelling white.
You can see her even at a great distance,
by her posture, problem-solving,
meticulous, and nothing,
not snow-melt water shards, nor rolling rocks,
nor glacial current battering her thighs,
is going to hurry her; her posture
manic in its stillness,
in the surge uproariously tumbled all around her;
and she makes it fine.

Friday, July 24, 1992.

The icy water bends like molten glass,
impressing weight across the curvature of rock,
descends and breaks, falls, and then,
and then, the poem by Robert Kroetsch
entrusting to the reader's mind
the memory of other falls,
with minimal intrusion, shapes perception
and the water's fall,
and the waters fall
like glass.

Saturday, July 25, 1992.

There in the shattered bright of a split boulder
held in the clawed shadows of moss campion,
wormwood and prickly saxifrage, among
the clumped gravel, mouse-eared chickweed and Arctic heather,
lapland rosebay and snow cinquefoil,
mountain aven and bilberry,
the caribou scat, the beginnings of soil —
in the lee of our tent, the improbable remnant
of a Canadian flag, stretched in the caught air, flutters.
And when I turn out in the wounded night, it is there,
still, in the taloned rock, a dried-blood swirl on spectral white.
In the grey of the morning, dry with the promise of change,
I hold the retrieved remnant to the chill breeze;
it measures a yard high on the halyard side,
and a metre long on the luff, with the centre gone,
and only the flash of the right-angled tatter —
a white band rising, flayed red
at the edge,
bleached bone and the unreal colour of nail polish —
declare the strategy
of its absent design; after coffee
I bury it under a rock that is clenched in lichen,
replacing the rock exactly,
as if it had never been moved.

Sunday, July 26, 1992.

From a shale perch by the top of Hidden Falls,
you can see the Panorama reappear as a distant maze
in the meadow below, and beyond Gas Drum Flats
the horizon like music is shaping the sky,
enthralled with the air
in its evasion of words in your mind.

Today a caribou yearling,
uncertain of danger, imperious,
then darting for cover through canyons of boulders,
curious, returning, trotting and grazing, affecting
    indifference,
stayed with us for over an hour, followed us
across an unnamed river and around a lake,
both which I named for my daughters,
unable to settle on who would be lake, and who, the river;
the river a tumble of blues among rock, like a song,
and the lake, a lavender blue in the depths,
from the unmelted ice beneath crystal green riffs
on the surface; Ginny named the caribou Luke
and both of us felt twinges of grief, fearing,
ingenuous and inquisitive, it would encounter destruction,
its lesson, from us.

In the evening, as the sun circled north,
while Ginny worked on her Katannilik Journal,
her book of the place of the falls,
her daily account, including flowers and field notes
and map points projected, achieved, and spaces for pictures,
I toyed with my pen, like an amulet
against the silence, and revelled in silence
when the words wouldn't come,
and searched in the landscape for language, the words,
to capture the blues, and the movements and stillness,
to contain the horizon and capture the story,
and after a while, brisk with the cold,
I entered the tent, zipped myriad zippers,
crawled into the warmth of my sleeping bag,
aqua and mauve, improbable colours for warmth,
and read aloud by the dying light
from *Howards End* until Ginny dozed off
and I drifted, through words, into dream.

Monday, July 27, 1992.

Written in pen on the inside wall of an emergency shelter
where the Itijjagiac and the Kuujuaq meet:
"Alan Kilabuk and Renee Wissink returning to Pang by dogteam
after having arrived in Lake Harbour
via Nettiling, Amadjuaq & Mingo Lakes.
Return via Iqaluit & Opingivik.
Expect to reach Pang in 8–10 days.
April 22/92. All well!"
Written below, in pencil, in another hand:
"They made the return trip in 7 days!"
I have added the quotation marks;
the points of exclamation
are from the original text.

Tuesday, July 28, 1992.

Dropping from the geomorphics of illimitable boulder debris
to paleontology
and the smell of green,
we put away binoculars and compass
and ration out the remaining exposures
on our borrowed camera;
in the descent from one vast amphitheatre to another
of the river's convolution,
carved by ancient ice and the ineluctable
working of winds and the weather,
each draped in the worn velvet
of distant vegetation, there is no middle distance;
the world is immediate or far away,
the gravel underfoot of lateral moraines
grown over with the moss of centuries,
the mountains worn to roundness,
sheared here and there by tumbled rock,
circumscribing; braced awkwardly

against my pack, I catch my breath
between this huge and intimate arena
and the majesty of flowers at my feet,
our own shadows rumpled on the ground;
in the middle, only, is perception,
with the world, at hand or distant, all around.

Wednesday, July 29, 1992.

It's hard to make love on the tundra
with Arctic willows no more than a hand's breadth high
and twisted birches sprawled across the sediment
and mosquitoes inquisitive
to the point of rudeness and lichens
scratchy and moss damp and no shadows
and gravel sharply protruding
among the wildflowers and waterfalls
and wind rushing in the distance
and the prints of caribou and a single
wolf the only witness.

Thursday, July 30, 1992.

A brief history of time
is the catchy phrase describing Hawking's book of ultimate realities.
I have been carrying it from the beginning
and religiously do readings from it every evening,
enough to finish by the journey's end,
although I don't think much
of time-space events so vast or small
they have to be described by zeroes;
actually, I skim a lot, and write notes in the margins,
on the endleafs and inside covers,
concerning the Arctic of our own experience,
our place in time
and the history of its passing.

Friday, July 31, 1992.

Dancing naked on the tundra,
a fifty-two-year-old man,
gaunt as a marionette, loose-limbed,
prancing, howling, dancing
naked as a caribou carcass
in spring snow —

Ginny is fishing in the frigid waters
where the Cascade meets the Kuujuaq;
she believes in fishing the way I believe in tent rings,
the ones I backtracked to this morning
just to be for a while with stone circles,
the stones half buried in lichen,
some nearly obscured as the earth
moves skyward; she believes
the fish are there,
indifferent to enthusiasm
or desire.

The lure gets fouled in the icy depths
and a fifty-two-year-old naked man,
lean from two weeks carrying a pack across
the tundra, dives deep and springs for shore
in a single action, a marionette,
improvising emotion,
yodelling with the joy of being alive
and the imprecations
of aching indignity.

Saturday, August 1, 1992.

We stopped short in the evening
because we saw the camp ahead.
Walking through the morning, by the river bend,

we saw the Inuit tent was across the Kuujuaq,
where it meets the Livingstone —

white canvas from the Co-Op,
a wedge, straight-edged,
no fly, no mosquito netting;
old man sitting on a crate
carving memories from stone —

we leapt salutations, shouted attention
across the turbulence;
drank tea
and admired his concentration,
a hunter of shadows and light.

Only as we moved away
did he hear and see us
across the wide gap
where the rivers merge,
Kuujuaq, meaning the big river,
and the other, named after a man.
He responded to our waves with a wave
and we moved on.

In Lake Harbour, two days later,
in the Co-Op, in the coffee shop,
we met our elderly Inuk,
a young bearded botanical artist
from Alberta. We admired his pictures,
delicate sketches, pencil lines and ghostly vibrant
     washes,
ink and colour and the subtle weave of paper
articulating vital fragments of terrain
we had travelled over;
but the most precise and haunting picture
was the one in our minds he had made

of an elderly Inuk apparently carving
at the confluence of two powerful rivers.

Sunday, August 2, 1992.

Awakening on the final morning,
and the warmed air is alive with mosquitoes;
Lake Harbour is still heavy hours away, last evening
it was another world,
another galaxy.

We rehearse our history on the final walk,
mythology already shaping memory
and the stories we concede in common
prepare themselves for other stories
of the Kuujuaq and Itijjagiac,
of Katannilik and Baffin,
of the northern territories and the Arctic
that we'll meet.

In the retreat of a startled caribou
on the edge of town, in Arctic images
of such enduring magnitude,
the vast, familiar universe
gathers like a thought free-forming
and time falls briefly into place,
distance and direction, into line.

Monday, August 3, 1992; Postscript
Kimik Co-Op

You guys, he said in a voice so low
I almost thought he meant someone else,
name everything. I go all over
up there in winter
with no map no compass.

We don't name everything.
Ginny at the next table with Dennis Budgen,
correlating the pressed flowers in her journal
with the perfect renderings on his sketch pad,
conferring with Maddy and Jo, checking in books,
getting the words right —
Moosa Akavak
explains: Gas Drum Flats, we call that
the river lowland beside the big hill,
that place up there.
I go there
by snowmobile.
We always go there; always.
I thought of tent rings, undisturbed, and caribou trails beside the
    river.
We are always there, he said; listen,
he is offering always
as if it were another language,
like an amulet or rune. Listen;
you can hear the waters
falling in the summer wind,
and the river's rush in winter
beneath the frozen undulations of the world.

5

ULTIMA THULE AND THE METAPHYSICS OF ARCTIC LANDSCAPE

*T*HIS IS A TRUE STORY; it is happening still. I am dressed warmly, wearing on my feet, over wool socks and duffel slippers, caribou leggings with the fur side in and doubled polar bear kamiks, one layer with the hair inside and the outer layer with the hair exposed. On my hands I wear sealskin mittens over wool undergloves. My parka is trimmed against the wind with Arctic wolf. I am wearing caribou pants over expedition-weight Capilene underwear, with a Gore-Tex wind suit under a down jacket over an Aran sweater, under a quilted canvas greatcoat. I am staring into the eyes of a wolf on the Arctic snow, with only the length of my shadow between us.

This is a true story, an event so rare it is already anecdotal around Lake Harbour. He came to me across the sea ice, through a tidal wall of sea-green ice across the bay, loped over the hard-packed February snow, strong and angular in motion, stopped so close I could hear the wind in his fur, see his teeth glisten with breathing. There is no fear. He yawns, sniffs, bobs his head from the shoulder, paces, eyes luminous in the evening light, cast from the horizon behind us. Graeme Dargo, beside me, cocks his rifle; the wolf edges closer. We breathe in unison. Graeme fires in the air. The wolf spins at the echo but settles so close he can hear my whisper, the urgency. Leave before the hunters come. Graeme and I begin to talk in normal voices; the wolf listens to the air, searching for the words. We turn over the snowmobile engines. He bristles and settles again, waiting. A hunter appears in the distance; a light and then sound. The wolf turns, his eyes fill with the hunter. Simanek Sagiatuk stops fifty feet away, killing his engine. The wolf walks toward him. The hunter shoots. We help him, an old man, lift it into his komatik. *Amaruq*, wolf. *Inuk*, hunter. *Qallunaaq*, watchers.

When outsiders travel to the Arctic something special happens; not always but enough to be remarkable. In contours of the diverse landscape visitors discover aspects of themselves not usually accessible. It is as if elusive worlds we build within turn inside out and, separated from us, reside in the austere climate of the Arctic, the enthralling texture of its light, the visceral impact of its apparent emptiness. In a secular age, in which it seems imagination is our only access to immortality, sometimes in the landscape as an emanation of our desire is the absolute stillness of time, which is all we really wanted after all. Not heaven in a grain of sand, but intimations of our continuity with lichen crumbling underfoot, the air breaking in thunder, hunger satisfied; not cosmology but the possibilities of being. For some this is the closest we come to reconciliation with our understanding of the universe. In Arctic landscape there is no other world that is not also ours; anything imagined can be real.

I know it is a trick of desiccating tissue, but when the human body turns to artifact through heat, the mouth parts tighten in a silent scream, while in extreme cold the face sustains a smile or expression of surprise. The body itself, wrenched from landscape, seems invariably distracted. In a display case he shares with the woman assumed to be his mother, the infant Greenland mummy, in the web of cranial fibre glistening through the sockets of his eyes, argues not the body but death itself as artifact. I am bent so close to the transparent wall between us, the grid across the periphery of my vision is the pattern of my lashes against the glass. This is unlike the pictures I have seen: photographs fail to capture the startled human moment, endlessly repeating in diminutive repose. He is fully dressed in skins of caribou, eaten centuries ago perhaps by the woman he accompanies on display. In the Museo de la Momias in Guanajuato, an infant lies behind a crude glass wall beside its mother who is dressed in bridal white. It is her you focus on, not the baby; the humiliation of her death, seared by the hot sand into elegant features. At the Grönlands Nationalmuseum in Nuuk, what you notice most about the woman is the depression across her abdomen where the tiny child lay through frozen centuries before being turned outward to embrace the world.

On the way to Tuktoyaktuk, after thirty days paddling the Mackenzie, we stopped for tea and bannock among the ruins at Kittigazuit. Virginia and I, nearing the end of our trip, summer 1989: I said when I die, look for me here, between stones and the shore, in wind-driven snow, among driftwood fragments, mouse-eared chickweed, and prickly saxifrage, among the borrowed bones of a hundred generations. She drank her tea and said nothing. The rain was silver, and cold spread across the landscape like an old discarded shroud.

The pages of Aritha van Herk's *Places Far from Ellesmere* are cut unevenly to remind you, page by page, that you are reading, that she is reading as well as writing, that *Anna Karenina* is being read on Ellesmere Island. Perhaps, she thinks, you can un/read her, set her free. There on that desert island, between the harebells and the blue dreaming of glaciers. Perhaps you have already taken this trip, and are only following your future.

In the desert climate of the Canadian Arctic, for it is not desert everywhere, snow falls sideways, lifting with the wind and flooding the terrain with direction while the sky is piercing blue. In the slow Arctic evening the limits of opacity, smouldering, crumble, galling gold-vermillion across evanescent landscape. At night, above the whirling flood, you can see the refusal of God to exist. When you see nothing between the stars, you *see* nothing — for a God who created everything ex nihilo, you would have to see the absolute as an unconditioned absence, everywhere. It is comforting in time to know there is no God; God's only hope is human consciousness. The wind articulates the landscape with an aura of snow; and beyond you the sky is piercing blue.

Rudy Wiebe writes in his contemplation of the Arctic *Playing Dead* that Arctic ice is water, sometimes pretending to be land. But ice in the Arctic, he might have said, is land that pretends for a few months in an annual cycle to be open water. In the long Arctic cold, solid rivers arch above their hollow courses and ice cascades in fixed waves across translucent cliffs; imagine colour as the dangerous quality of light on infinite varieties of white. The heart could hardly bear such optic slendour were it not wrapped in flesh against the lethal cold. On sea ice, especially, the metamorphosis is deadly, incomplete. Across the blue-black steaming of an open lead, dazzling silver beckons like a harsh and brilliant watercolour winterscape by David Milne, but we stay patiently to seaward, within reach of the jagged floe edge, like a hand-tinted etching, waiting for the tide to turn, the lead to close, for ice to be ice again.

The wolf I saw in a magazine — this is from a poem by Robbie Newton Drummond —

> glances at the flotsam
> on my writers desk —
>
> lopes out across the empty page,
> becomes what
> wind carves
> for its shadow.

It is possible with words to shape dreams of the dead. The wistful ghost of George Cartwright, an eighteenth-century Labrador en-trepreneur from England, is left by death an observer on the edge of time — until a recent novel by John Steffler lets him back in through acts of narrative grace. The historical Cartwright invented for himself an additional six years of bloodletting adventure beyond the ten he actually spent among the Inuit, turning documentary ingenuously to fiction in a book he published by subscription in 1792. With temporal integrity in abeyance, it seems inevitable, at least to Steffler, that Cartwright's ghost should be refused eter-nity — until time becomes substantial once again by narrative design. Final release is accomplished by Steffler, in *The Afterlife of*

George Cartwright, through emendation of a grisly scene begun two centuries before, as a great white bear consumes what's left of Cartwright's unhallowed remains:

> with each bite, as more of him vanishes, a feast of new beauty appears. Small ferns and mosses curly as hair spring from the cracks in the rock where he was sitting.
>
> The bear devours one leg as far as the thigh, then the other, turning its head sideways like a dog to crunch the bones in the back of its jaws.
>
> Then it plunges its snout between Cartwright's legs, up through his hips, burrowing under his ribs. The bear's white head is a wide pointed brush, moving from side to side, painting him out, painting the river, the glittering trees in.

Sometimes we watch, and in silence become what we see. In remembering blood we recall the future, our death, when time and space are indistinguishable and we indivisible from place. In the Arctic, intimations of another world shape the dreamer dreaming, the writer writing; we separate from psychological realities, metaphysical desires; in metamorphosis or visionary conceit we see ourselves, infinite and eternal, shadows without people, belonging to the landscape.

Dreaming of sleep is sometimes enough to keep us awake.
To be dead is a contradiction in terms, an existential paradox.

There are different ways of saying this; but it can be no worse to inflict on history generalizations much the same as history has thrown at us. British interest in the Arctic of North America had to do with expansion of Empire, and the display of British values (the Arctic was an impediment); American interest, with a projection of the American dream, the display of American ideals (the Arctic was a testing ground); Canadian interest, with sovereignty and administration, the display of order and of its limitations (the Arctic, mapped, became a wilderness).

Curious, to found ourselves on acts of finding, written into narratives, onto maps; as if we were there already, waiting to be found. And now the writer is explorer; not the other way around. Since Franklin perished wordlessly, with only marginalia on an Admiralty document to mark his death, although his passing fills volumes, while Charles Francis Hall left scattered notes concerning his impending murder in the Davis Strait, and other Americans, from Kane through Greeley down to Robert Peary became metafictional devices, the signifiers signified, since Robert Falcon Scott wrote down his dying thoughts before becoming ice, and now adventurers like Ranulph Fiennes, Robert Swan, and Richard Weber record the ordinary practicalities of current polar exploits, it has fallen on literary writers — or been the challenge taken up by literary writers — to mediate between the Arctic and the outside, to transform themselves into Arctic landscape, and not the other way around.

Picture this: a proscenium frame; a grey-blue sky receding from an origami iceberg that rides the folded contours of a paper sea. There are only hints of cloud; the ice, the water, and the sky neither attract nor repel the hidden sun. There is a play of planes and surfaces, some flat and some perpendicular, aslant to catch external light. The sea has no depth, yet colour rises through it. This is a painting by Doris McCarthy. I imagined it before I saw it. I thought that it would be by Lawren Harris or Toni Onley. You can see through the iceberg if you look carefully. And this, an etching by David Blackwood: the sea opens; there is a huge whale in the foreground, hard-edged against the dark pellucid depths; in the ink-blue sky an iceberg looms, and in its lea a burning ship, like a brief wound, lists into its own shadow; the iceberg cuts deep behind the whale, a twisting spectral imminence. The whale is straining particles of the sea through its baleen grille; this looks for all the world, from your perspective, an unholy grin.

I have been so often in imagination at the confluence of the Thelon and the Hanbury, I can remember the sound of the wind in every season. I can smell the driving sleet, the snow, the sun-bleached gravel, the poignance of new vegetation growing on generations of ancestral detritus, and I can see what I would see of the Barrens in all directions, but I do not see myself; although if I look carefully, I can see in the foreground, as I turn, a shadow without feet in the shape of a man.

What does it take to belong to the land, how do you grow a native place, how do you make the visionary real? We are all outsiders in a world where time is the measure of moment, and duration the moment of being (then no one is at home). But think for a minute, if time is indivisible, simultaneous, then your minute is forever. Look at the night sky: you can see time. This is not an analogy; time is spatial, spread out limitless and numberless. You can read your watch in the light of the stars. Everything you see is past. Everything you see is present.

Kristjana Gunnars said, about *The Prowler*, about Iceland, potentially there is no reality. History is from somewhere; geography is something else. The Arctic, there, is everything — her facial expression, elusive, quizzical; amused that place could be so easily removed from time, and then reintegrated with an enigmatic shrug.

Four decades after Helge Ingstad left his thriving law practice in Norway to live as a trapper in the Barrens, from 1926 through 1930, he discovered the remnants of Leif Eriksson's Vineland settlement at L'Anse aux Meadows on the coast of northern Newfoundland; with Anne Stein Ingstad, his wife, and a team of archaeologists, he uncovered the ruins of seven houses and countless details of "white Inuit" life in the year A.D. 1000, far from Greenland, far from Iceland, far from Viking Europe. The site is now on the UNESCO World Heritage List.

We are all outsiders who cannot read proclivities of the wind in rock and snow. If you stand deeply immersed within the temporal surge, yet rooted to the solid ground, by academic fiat, no one is at home — even native peoples are in exile. In *The Great Journey: The Peopling of Ancient America* Brian M. Fagan writes of an Arctic inimical to human destiny:

Bering Strait is a desolate, windy place. Even in summer the winds can howl through smoky mists, cutting visibility to a few yards. Savage winters last for nine months in these latitudes. For eight months a year the strait is ice-covered as far south as 60 degrees N. It is a somewhat unspectacular place. . . .

His discourse on what he calls Beringia builds from the possibilities of crossing savage wastes from Asia to America in skin boats or on a land bridge. But he is talking about people fully culturated and acclimatized to what from his perspective are extreme conditions — they may have been moving *with* the cold, not away from it, back and forth across the ice, where and when hunting was good, footing firm, insects absent, food preserved, clothing warm, and shelter a carapace of whalebone and sod or glistening snow. They were not there, then, nor now, here, by default.

In the opening paragraph of *Agaguk* Yves Thériault describes "the endless tundra, flat and monotonous like the winter sky, without horizon and without trees." It is necessary to understand the limitation of his words, to conceive a north so empty.

The closing stanzas of Frank Scott's *Letters from the Mackenzie River* wrap similar appropriations of the landscape in a beautiful enigma that collapses into the emptiness of poetic argument:

> A river so Canadian
>   it turns its back
>   on America
>
> The Arctic shore
>   receives the vast flow
>   a maze of ponds and dikes
>
> In land so bleak and bare
>   a single plume of smoke
>   is a scroll of history.

Not every writer finds the Arctic barren. Some write the landscape into literature; but some, a few, risk the gape of gravity and soar — and write their language into Arctic landscape, and in their writing carry readers to the very edge of territories undreamed in the dreams of others. In their ecstatic, sometimes haunted records of encounters with the Arctic's awesome beauty or its subtle grace are implications, intimations, of a visionary world more real than actuality. Call this, their envisioned world, Ultima Thule, in deference to tradition; see it as an alternate dominion yet to be discovered; name it as the psyche's other home.

Some explore with words, their extremities of thought. In records of earliest exploration are descriptions of places yet to be achieved.

Some explore with words, whose imperatives to venture north include discovery of self within a metaphysical design.

Addressing Arctic landscape through imagination allows the writer writing to be metaphor, and the visionary world to be real.

Whales of the night air pass over us (J. Michael Yates in *The Great Bear Lake Meditations*):

> The mad arctic light of the outside finally finds me through the crusted snows of my skin. I'm coming soon to the end of me, to the membrane which contains all my mortal remains. The needle of my compass points always north like the finger of a prophet until I become north, and, like a shot swan, it bewilders in terrible circles. There is no object in the white landscape upon which to triangulate. Hunter and weapon merge, and the quarry whirls at the box-canyon wall to battle the nothing at all behind him.

Saturday, March 13, 1993. Sometimes you know you're living the future; that you, today, will reappear from the convoluted labyrinth of memory, perhaps transformed in the last and perfect moment of your life or possibly in guises appropriated by an echoing event yet undetermined; you know this reaching moment will come around again. The snow streaks horizontally across the fields and lacerates your face, whirls against your feet, and you run the road from Bellrock into the swaggering embrace of the worst winter storm since 1896. You are training for Boston. The words are like magic. Training for Boston. And the snow searing like needles of acid, this is the training effect. In a country blessed with the drama of seasons, sweet are the uses of adversity.

First Lake Road. From Bellrock. Pale green and nameless, a region which did not appear on a map until 1910. I'm quoting from *In the Skin of a Lion*, a book I in some ways admire. I know this part by heart. This is the part where my own world is written into fiction, and out of it. Maps of an unremembered landscape, the past authenticated with a publication date, names forgotten from decades, centuries, and millennia past — in Michael Ondaatje's eloquent denial of the richness of my heritage, my ancestral place, I become, myself, a literary artifact. Running deep within the storm, I refuse eloquence. I cannot tell my own extremities from the snow, the wind, the cold. I am not from somewhere else; unhyphenated, I am here.

Two weeks ago, at forty below, crossing Katannilik from Lake Harbour to Iqaluit, where last summer Virginia and I had backpacked through the tumultuous tangle of sweet-smelling tundra and toyed with winter imagery, imagining, I dreamed of this running, today, of training like this in the toughest conditions. My eyes blistering behind clumped ice binding the lashes, skimming the Arctic landscape on a thrashing Yamaha at the apparent speed of light, catching glimpses of the others, Elijah Padluq, Moosa Akavak, and Graeme Dargo, twisting through tunnels of snow, I thought about training for Boston, the thousands of runners all over the world, in a hundred languages, perhaps none of them dressed in caribou skins, who were training, were training, who would gather to run, and I thought of running in Bellrock, and life there on the Baffin snow appeared seamless and whole. In the indecipherable whiteness I was battered cold, self-consciously Canadian, and curiously content. When we stopped for steaming tea and bannock near Panorama Falls, I couldn't think of anything to say. No one says anything. The sloughing wind outlines the frozen landscape; the present tense seems absolute.

I have been waiting a long time to write this. Whitman was thirty-eight when he published *Leaves of Grass*, and I search among its pages for understanding of the Arctic mission pursued by America on his behalf; for surely it was an arrogant man, a poet, who inspired his countrymen's pursuit of Franklin, to sing of their own hearts set to the bitter wind in small boats, their own blood beating through the veins of an expiring dream. Surely it was Whitman, an arrogant man, not vain but certain, proud, who entering the vocabulary of his country-men dreamed new dreams and sent them wandering among the sinews of his vision in search of words to document America.

Albert Johnson. John Hornby. Some men explore in silence. Make silence their only code. Wrap themselves in it; until death invades their silence, and they violently expire. This leaves others to expropriate their solitude, to make them language, articulate their lives in docu-mentary narratives, flashback metafiction, poems, contemplative es-says. If the silences of women turned virtual reality in the same way, if the silence of the dispossessed were spoken, if the wordlessness of Arctic landscape were uttered so assiduously, we might yet find a song to celebrate.

Trapper Johnson's mad refusal to become a word, for which both Rudy Wiebe and Robert Kroetsch articulate a sacrificial death, and the lethal recklessness of John Hornby's unwritten eccentricity, which haunts like a legend we cannot grasp in book after book of the Arctic Barrens (especially in George Whalley's meticulous adventure in which Hornby becomes, in his silence, a distinctively Canadian motif) — the recluse and the renegade, our unuttered heritage — both leave us to acquit ourselves in literary paradigms.

Ultima Thule is a projection of private and collective aspirations, a paradox, just beyond the last place to be reached. Figuratively it exists; literally it is a fantasy.

Pythias, a Greek explorer, a contemporary of Aristotle, first envisioned Thule as a realm of warmth and perpetual sunshine over the northern horizon. A Roman, Seneca, made it, in his speculations on the north, Ultima Thule. The medieval British commandeered the phrase, and thence it came to us, associated principally with polar exploration but also, especially in the current mode, with chimerical versions of the Northwest Passage such as Stan Rogers's one warm line through a land so wide and strange, Gwendolyn MacEwen's bathetic giant virginal strait crushing violators forever in her stubborn loins, or Yates's antithesis of the poignant absence inside us wherever we go, around and around the Earth.

But there is a distinction between Thule and the Northwest Passage in the shaping mind of Canada. It is important to know this. Adventurers of the past who sought the east in a westerly direction found the north an impediment (and the south, distracting). The Arctic was not a destination; of only incidental consequence. But explorers of the longitudes, from Pythias to Robert Peary, dreamed of pinnacles, not passageways. They created the figurative reality of polar regions where meridians of geography and personality converge. The Arctic was a place to be; visionary, not linear. Not means, but end. Ultima Thule was about the substantiality of dreams; not a dream to be endured. It is the difference between being and becoming, presence (however unlikely) and imminence (however promising); for Canada, between a real imagined timeless place and the unreality of process (identity forever in transition); for Canada the difference between Arctic landscape as a visionary metonym and a dissociating metaphor.

I watch Virginia painting watercolours, turning coloured water into
    light.
She works at home from a photograph that has been enlarged, cut up, reshaped and taped, reprographed to enhance or to obscure blocks and lines of colour.
She works on Arches 140-pound cold-pressed paper.

The photograph itself she took with a Leica M2 on Baffin, on a summer day so cold her fingers stiffened when she removed her gloves and the shutter slurred, giving the impression that the person at a distance, upright against the freezing rain beneath my pack, was about to disappear among the muted colours and the softened lines. It all comes back on paper; in the depths of light within.

Perhaps the notion of Arctic narrative as a linear quest will self-destruct; and we, absolved from the structures of grammar and story, might find among words the power of silence; in the subversion of imminence, secular grace. With the stillness of time, discontinuity falls into place. There might be in the glistening details a vision of silence, in stubborn particulars the pleasures of chaos, the pleasure through a shattered text of silvered estuaries, on Ellesmere, the pleasures of oblivion. Nothing I can say / will make words of nothing.

Potentially there is no reality, she says. Kristjana Gunnars says. Some Icelandic novels make no sense. They are not meant to make sense. . . . My father's people, the white Inuit, have always known that potentially they do not exist. The story is always somewhere else.

There is an ironic resonance to the title, in English, of Helge Ingstad's book on his experience in the Barrens — *The Land of Feast and Famine.* Ingstad describes his familiarity with rumours of John Hornby's disappearance; the remains of Hornby, Edgar Christian, and Harold Adlard were found along the Thelon while Ingstad was in the area; he knew the details from direct conversation with the investigating officer, Corporal Williams of the RCMP. Stories have it Hornby left behind some random passages, intended for an Arctic memoir. It was to be called "In the Land of Feast or Famine," according to notes filed by Corporal Williams, although no manuscript was found among Hornby's effects.

Canada, unhyphenated, held possible in imagination, reaches to the North Pole itself. But the exact pole is a singular zero, an algebraic integer or geometric dot; it is sheer essence, a swirl of white quite still upon the shifting ice cap, upon the spinning globe; the pole is time collapsed to a perfect arithmetic point, a geophysical matrix, a place that occupies no space; it is the intercalation from a speculative text upon the theoretically two-dimensioned (depthless) skin of Earth.

I own a poster copy of the Blackwood etching, autographed, and I have seen Harris paintings in the National Gallery and the McMichael Collection, and Toni Onley paintings reproduced in books — the mental composite I pictured of an origami icescape was displaced by works of Doris McCarthy, when I actually saw her *Iceberg Fantasies*, in a retrospective exhibition at the Gallery/Stratford in Stratford, Ontario. McCarthy's sequence, done in oil on canvas, does not capture the Arctic in a frozen gesture, as Harris sometimes does, nor re-create it as the distillation of emotion, as Blackwood does (does not impale or extrapolate); does not infuse a watercolour landscape with personality, as Onley does. Rather, McCarthy reveals an absolute stillness of light (that is there even when the world is apparently in motion), a defiant clarity of light, the depth of surfaces, and the luminescent surface of the Arctic deep. In my study in Bellrock I contemplate the imagined Arctic. I can shift my eyes without otherwise betraying movement from the computer screen, where I observe ideas like Arctic willows creep and curl upon themselves, shift my eyes to a watercolour sketch by Dennis Budgen, and experience, in faint pencilled lines of wind around the Arctic cotton, implications of a landscape only he can see.

Violence is the language of secrets in Robert Kroetsch's "Poem of Albert Johnson," and death is a flowering:

> letting gunshot   into his best pursuer
> his self's shadow   dressed in red authority
> and after the quick exchanging   unspeakably dead
>
> and gone beyond all living   the silent man
> made the impossible crossing   the snowshoe pattern
> over the closed pass   into the caribou herd

that gave him a gap   out of the closing frame
the trap   forged by the roaring bush plane
out of six week's hunting   the silent man

having leapt their ring   walked back
and baited their pride   with his spent body
bought them the cry they sought   and only kept

his silence (we stand at his grave in Aklavik
mosquitoes swarming at our heads   like the posse
that slammed him   out of his last loading)

the poet of our survival   his hands and feet
frozen   no name on his dead mouth
no words betraying   either love or hate

Burial is everywhere a literary act; what remains of earth is eloquence.

Sometimes writers from the outside enter Arctic landscape as emanations of its lost uneasy dead, their words the voice of other travellers and visionaries who, buried, are already fiction. Or like Aritha van Herk, more directly they become its metaphysical reflection. Some write personality as landscape on which the sprawling Arctic story opens like a revelation; I am thinking especially of Barry Lopez and Rudy Wiebe. Some, like Al Purdy, see their ephemeral absurdity mirrored in an alien terrain (Purdy said: I needed something to write about so I went north — the Arctic, semiotic; the Arctic as context). Others write of their experience in the north as if lives depended on it; and others, of a quest within that would take the measure of the universe.

Aritha van Herk, flying from Resolute:

Ellesmere will appear like a languid body below you, the island only waiting finally to float into *geografictione* . . . You worry that your boots will give you blisters.

Al Purdy, dreaming lovers beside a Baffin river:

> . . . lying prone together
> where the purged green
> boils to a white heart
> and the shore trembles
> like a stone song.

Van Herk:

> passionately shaped water pouring itself down from
>   the perpetual glaciers of the Arctic . . .
> You are in love with Ellesmere. You are in love with
>   your hiking boots. . . .
> At last, again, you think you've found a home.
> You search out possible sites for your future grave.

I have been reading in *Time* the subset of Stephen Hawking's mind. Our atavistic impulse toward unity — nostalgia, as Camus describes it — Hawking takes literally in his struggle to contain the macrocosm and the microcosm in a single theory. But the model is confused. Because mathematics cannot handle infinity or eternity, he argues, we should cut them out, eliminate them from cosmological speculation. In so doing, Hawking now can prove that time moves forward; or, in staying still, that we move backward. I'd like Hawking to understand that time in my experience does not move at all; with no beginning, no end, it simply is. And we fall hurtling through. If we break his solipsistic model, eternity and infinity are indivisible, the context within which we travel perpetually from order to chaos and order again, or chaos to order and chaos again. It is we who move, not time. If we could move at the speed of light, we would catch up with ourselves not moving in that brief moment before we burst into oblivion.

Hold this book, *Oksitartok*, which means beautiful mind, carefully; printed in the 1960s, the leaves slide away from dried-out perfect binding and, unpaginated, shuffle toward entropy in your hands. The author's biography at the back, recorded in reverse chronology so that his life seems a discontinuous accumulation of surprises, projects the date of his death as 1989. There was a time, in the sixties, when dying was romantic; but the author, Norman Elder, is still alive. Unlike Steffler's Cartwright or the narrator of van Herk's *Places Far from Ellesmere*, he has so far evaded becoming metaphor, although evasion itself is a literary device. In the High Arctic landscape he, too, moves frenetically toward stillness.

The summer after Purdy's celebrated sojourn in 1965, Elder conned his way from Resolute to Alert, even dropped in on the American air base at Thule in northwest Greenland, and in a spontaneous documentary recorded random selections from everything that crossed his mind, which he later published privately and sold from the trunk of his car at hunt and country clubs around Toronto. In a manic parody of contemporary Arctic narratives, Elder accounts for himself on his tour as a sociologist, construction worker, archaeologist, scientist on the Polar Shelf Project, officer in the U.S. military, geologist, and anthropologist. He also, with ironic detachment, contemplates his death in a variety of panoramic Arctic vistas, awakening dreams of desert heat and efflorescent forests of the Amazon.

Arctic North America entered Elizabethan consciousness as both obstacle and void, its meaning only in the aftermath of its experience. There was little romance, although now the names of thirteen commanding officers, twelve of them British, perseverate across the years; a few anecdotes, words in brief clusters, a few apocryphal images, pictures at the edge of schoolbook memories, resonate. Whatever the reality, their names now seem indigenous, primordially our own (there is no accounting for the anonymous dead):

Martin Frobisher, 1576, 1577, 1578
John Davis, 1585, 1586, 1587
George Weymouth, 1602

John Knight, 1606   disappears ashore; Labrador
Henry Hudson, 1610–11   still adrift in Arctic mist
Thomas Button, 1612–13
William Gibbons, 1614
Robert Bylot and William Baffin, 1615, 1616
William Hawkridge, 1619
Jens Munk, 1619–20   three survive, including Munk
Luke Foxe, 1631
Thomas James, 1631–32

According to Walter Kenyon's posthumous book *Arctic Argonauts*, only four of these parties overwintered. During the next phase of Arctic exploration, what he calls the scientific age between 1819 and 1858, thirty-two expeditions stayed through at least one winter (these figures do not acknowledge survival rates). He also observes: "between the battle of Waterloo and the outbreak of the Crimean war, the exploration of arctic Canada was virtually completed." This seems odd, coming from the curator of New World Archaeology at the Royal Ontario Museum, incongruously suggesting someone unfamiliar with dreams of the dead.

At the Scott Polar Research Institute in Cambridge, England, the most valued artifacts are books. There are also letters from the heroic past, ink scoring aging paper with boyish sentiments and awkward eloquence. These are behind glass, on rotating display. Strategically, against walls, in alcoves or among shadows, there are authentic skis and poles made from wood, thermal clothing made from wool, cumbersome mechanical equipment; all seem strangely anachronistic, in an environment of marble and veneer, distancing us from the landscape they were instrumental in exposing. There is a diorama, using Shackleton's original supplies, the labels now faded, greased with a layer of clinging dust, history irredeemably out of reach (or is this the Scott diorama in Christchurch; or Amundsen's in Tromsö? The colours then, less plastic, seem muted and far away, in any case). But in the stacks of the SPRI, as it is familiarly known, we find this other landscape, the landscape of endless interpenetrating sentences that polar regions generate impassively and leave for readers to explore. It is there we spend our time; then, febrile among words, we adjourn with temporary friends to the Prince of Wales on Trumpington to talk a while in the present tense, allowing the Arctic to become visceral in memory before we return to research and the written wilderness.

In the brief years following his retirement, my father tabled an elaborate genealogy that converged in his union with my mother and branched out again to include his grandchildren's generation, with space for further entries. Buried among the coded names and dates is Edward, his father's stepbrother, a surgeon. In 1878, when my father's father Austin was nine years old, three books appeared in London bookstores, born out of the last major British assault on the Arctic. One of these, *Shores of the Polar Sea: A Narrative of the Arctic Expedition of 1875–6*, was written by Edward L. Moss, surgeon on HMS *Alert*, under the command of George Nares, who is generally credited with establishing British sovereignty over Ellesmere, which was passed eventually to Canada.

Nares, who published his own narrative of the voyage, had sailed the Arctic in search of Franklin two decades earlier as second mate aboard the *Resolute*, under Horatio Austin. (The third account arising from the expedition was of a sledge journey under the command of Captain A. H. Markham that reached a record farthest north, beyond the Eighty-third Parallel, and for which Nares received a gold watch from Parliament.)

According to my father's genealogy, Austin was not a family name.

In his account of canoeing the Back River in 1987, an outraged Robert Perkins describes the travesty of four-foot lettering inscribed on a lakeside tundra landscape with small boulders: PELLY LAKE EXPEDITION 1979. Nearby, a bronze plaque celebrates Sir Henry Pelly, the governor of the Hudson's Bay Company after whom George Back named the lake. There are four other names on the plaque: Peter Dion, Tom Mawhinney, and David and Brian Pelly. Perkins sneers at a genealogical canoe trip, the commemoration of ego. I feel odd, reading that. I don't much like littering the terrain with alphabetical designs or chunks of chiselled metal, but I can understand the Pelly brothers. They were making connections. They wrote a modest narrative on the landscape, utterly obscure flamboyance, celebrating a man they never knew in a place he'd never been, because they were there, in the Arctic, and he had been alive once, and was in their blood.

The Perkins book, wrapped in a jacket with a full-moon spaceshot superimposed on a black stripe over a monochromatic blue icescape, is called *Into the Great Solitude: An Arctic Journey*. For Perkins, who names his canoe and travels with seven different hats, the Barrens offer a sort of fecund austerity in which to explore the experience of being himself, on his own, although he intersects several times with a film crew and also films himself in attitudes of profound contemplation and postures of ordinary survival. It is a fascinating book, deconstructing in almost every studied passage.

More self-consciously than most, Robert Perkins addresses other texts as he writes, intersecting with the words of Warburton Pike, shaping his course across the tundra among passages from George Back's *Narrative of the Arctic Land Expedition to the Mouth of the Great Fish River, 1833, 1834, and 1835*. Like other contemporary adventure-writers, he turns the Arctic of dreams, the Arctic of terror, into the Arctic of personal fulfillment and the escape from personality. These are not explorers of the soul, who share the land, but men whose books lean rakishly against one another on library shelves. Read Perkins, or James Raffan, or M. T. Kelly and you encounter again and again, in words from the past, the Douglas brothers, Hanbury, the Tyrrell brothers, Warburton Pike, George Back, Richardson, Franklin, Samuel Hearne. Each provides a gloss on those preceding. Even Hearne refers in passing to the *Journal of Jens Munk, 1619, 1620*. Text echoes text. From intertextual adventuring we conceive the Arctic wilderness a place where stories happen, written down, in effect, to articulate terrain like the lines of a topographical map. Narrative writes narrative. The rest is empty; solipsism is endemic.

High Arctic Wilderness Symposium, Monarch Park Collegiate, Toronto, January 22, 23, 1993, sponsored by the Wilderness Canoe
Association. Picture this: 800 Arctic enthusiasts have paid to see and
hear seventeen slide shows and two Inuuk speakers. Virginia and I talk
about backpacking through Katannilik. Doug Wilkinson, a filmmaker,
shows slides from the forties through the eighties, illuminating many
trips and several lengthy sojourns in the Baffin region. His book *Land
of the Long Day* records a year he spent forty years ago with the family
of Paul Idlout, one of the speakers. They hug at the front of the
auditorium and the audience applauds. We have shared a man's lifetime
experiences as a visitor in the Arctic, beautifully articulated in studied
images and casual commentary; we share in his embrace with the Arctic
man who was a child in his pictures. There is an explosion of emotion;
it has to do with the converging of divergent lives, with watching.

Doug Wilkinson closes by saying that we should not confuse population density with possession; nor openness with absence. What we
gather to celebrate as wilderness is not wilderness to the Inuit. I leave
the darkened auditorium, thinking wilderness a morbid notion, our
slides like game we mount on shining walls for public admiration,
documenting only us.

Overriding theological implications of the word, James Raffan argues
you can learn "nativity." *Become* native to a place. He believes this. His
argument: faith born out of his experience on the rivers of the Barrens,
his desire to become what he beholds. An old friend of mine, Hugh
Stewart, who has paddled many Arctic rivers, argued otherwise. Over
lunch in Ottawa he said the Arctic is separate from our knowing; to
give yourself to something is not the same as to belong.

Consider the words of Fred Breummer:
We travelled from nowhere to nowhere in a world all white,
eleven dogs, a long sled, a fur-clad Inuk and I.

Reading that, I return to Breummer's photographs, the Arctic caught
in some of the most striking postures of violence and repose recorded

on paper. His polychromatic images haunt, his black-and-whites enervate; but I realize, you *read* the photographs in his large-scale book *The Arctic World*, his autobiographical *Arctic Memoirs*, his other books. You do not observe or regard or survey; you are positioned, the content is positioned, you are led into the picture as text and see what the author wants to be seen, as he wants you to see it. And everything else is spectral. There is always a documentary subject; the picture is verb; you are the object. The background is colour and texture and light; the Arctic, extending from nowhere, a world all white. You do the haunting.

Writing as a white Inuk, Kristjana Gunnars describes the pleasures of reading an incomprehensible text, prowling among the endless configurations of what seems to be a very limited alphabet. In the wonderful confluence of language and narratives below, an entry from *Barrenland Beauties* by Page Burt, the story changes as the nexus of **title** and *Latin* (after exposition, historical digression, and authorial aside, all in English) submerges in a Kitengmiut dialect of Inuktitut (where Franklin achieves knighthood, English syllables press against meaning, the possessive is transformed, and the joke is lost or obscured).

Rock Tripe: *Umbilicaria*, sp.

These are the black leathery-looking lichens adhering to many rocks in our area, growing best on non-calcareous rocks, often on surfaces with high glacial polish.

On their trek across the Barrens from the Hood River to Fort Enterprise, the starving men of the Franklin expedition of 1819–1822 attempted to eat these lichens. As a result, nausea and diarrhea further weakened them — the lichens contained not only rock particles, but also high levels of acid, which irritated their digestive tracts. (Boiling in several changes of water, with the addition of baking soda, would have made them edible, but Franklin's men lacked the fuel, the time, and the baking soda.)

Rock Tripe. Ona kingnagitok kaguiyak naotiyukton oyakani, ilani allatkitlo naogatigiyutait. Ona Sir John Franklin aolaoyakpaktok nunaoyaliuhonilo nunapti 1821–22 milo ilangitaok avonga Katimanakmi avonga Winter Lakemot aolakpaton. Aolaktilogit akiagoakayakton. Nekehaigamik ona kagiuyak pokohogit oyakamit, kitolihakhogo hehaitomot imakmon negevaktat. [*Barrenland Beauties: Showy Plants of the Arctic Coast.* Inuktitut text by Susie Kapolak.]

I bought a book of obsessions recently from Arctic Ventures in Iqaluit, the store owned by Kenn Harper who wrote *Give Me My Father's Body.* This book has the unlikely title *Eastern North America as Seen by a Botanist: Pictorial (1. The Arctic Region).* The author is In-Cho Chung. There is no ISBN number. It was printed in Seoul, 1989. No publisher is indicated; further copies are available by writing In-Cho Chung at a Florida address. It costs $50 (Canadian) on Baffin. Hundreds of close-up colour photographs chronicle the author's quixotic rambling amid the flora of the High Arctic; the occasional panoramic shot or authorial aside in the captions make it clear this is a personal catalogue of In-Cho Chung's engagements at the intersection of knowledge and experience, recorded in a kind of static ecstasy. On page 86, plate note number 225–226 has been altered by hand and an erratum slip pasted in the margin. Even more touching is the emendation in the Selected Reference section, in a neat and tiny handscript, of the word *Ecological* to *Ecogeographical,* in the seemingly esoteric title of a 1977 Greenland publication: *Ecogeographical Classification of Arctic Vegetation Based on Shoots Density Determinations.* Such deliberate compromise with the capacity for technology to perpetuate error marks this book a document of the heart. I envision In-Cho Chung in Florida, bent over copies of his book as if each were an Arctic flower, meticulous in setting the record straight.

For more than half a century William Wordsworth reworked *The Prelude* as prologue to a larger work about himself that never happened. Although Coleridge is ubiquitous among the ice floes, distressed images of his doomed mariner a part of every sailors' gear, along with prayers of death and supplication, I can find no reference to Wordsworth in contemporary accounts, nor little in his sprawling essay-poems of the stolid capacity for courage, the intemperate modesty, of his compatriots, that made them in their annals splendid.

Wordsworth is an absence in the Arctic. Yet the paradox: as an absence he is real. Read Parry, read the Rosses, read especially the tortuous delights of that sad romantic, Sir Francis Belcher. There is a dissociation haunting the words, the desperate passages, of each recorded encounter with the Arctic of Wordsworth's contemporaries and immediate successors. They were never really there. Here.

At Kittigazuit, a day's paddle to the west of Tuktoyaktuk on the Beaufort Sea, a small Quonset hut beside the rubble beach is still used by the Cockney family as a camp. On the hill a deserted cabin made of logs brought up from Arctic Red looms vaguely sinister; they are smaller and more evenly turned than the giant driftwood debris along the shore. There are glass fragments in the windows, and the roof, although not waterproof, still functions architecturally. Among the tangled brush on the lower hillside are depressions in the ground with boulders at the edges. Some hide in their shadows remnants of caved-in whalebone roofs. It is hard to tell that people lived here for a hundred generations with only more luxuriant growth to mark their passage. Sometimes a thousand people at a time.

It is the same in the Kuujuaq on Baffin. When the pyramids were being contemplated and Stonehenge rose against the startled sky, people walked with caribou along this ancient valley; their modest monument a few small stones turned out of place, in circles, to hold the edges of their shelters aslant from the prevailing winds.

After the Northwest Passage proved impractical (M'Clintock credited Franklin with its possibility; a grisly epitaph), after M'Clure had sailed, drifted, walked the inchoate route from west to east, and Amundsen, waterborne except for overwintering in Goa Haven, claimed the prize, the British lost interest in collective Arctic endeavours. Franklin was the turning point. As rumours and remnants trickled back to England of this monstrous episode, the British turned to other things, foreign wars, Imperial expansion, catastrophes quite separable from a landscape they neither loved nor understood. (The brief exception: George Nares's expedition of 1875–6, which began in a panoply of chauvinistic enthusiasm and ended in ignominy verging on disgrace.) Scott and Shackleton, then Fiennes and Swan, would express British values without the burden or the benefit of official British sanction. Americans meanwhile used the humane imperatives of the Franklin search to invest their polar initiatives with an aura of heroic detachment.

Following Peary's claim on the North Pole in 1909, in the aftermath of which the reputation of his rival Dr. Frederick Cook was laid in ruins, then Amundsen's achievement of the South Pole in 1911, after which the vanquished Scott and his compatriots were sealed in ice, after Richard Byrd overflew both ends of the Earth, technological accomplishment overshadowing the human, American polar interest turned to corporate endeavours — the geodesic dome over the South Pole, the *Manhattan* smashing through Canadian waters, Polaris submarines on cruise-control under the polar ice cap.

Even after the poles collapsed, Vilhjalmur Stefansson's government-supported Canadian Arctic Expedition set out in 1913 to claim sovereignty over undiscovered territories beyond the Northwest Passage. Conflict between notions of Ultima Thule with a population of blond Inuit, fostered by Stefansson, and the methodological austerity of expedition scientists such as R. M. Anderson and Diamond Jenness, created legendary friction, highlighted by the sinking of the expedition ship off Siberia. After this the notion of Thule as the region of ultimate aspiration became almost entirely internalized, to be encountered only in a dream or vision, shared obliquely in descriptions of the landscape in poetry, adventure-narrative, or belletristic prose.

Auyuittuq. August 1991. After clambering through shadow tunnels, among huge boulders at the summit of Pangnirtung Pass, I emerge to catch my bearings and see Laura sitting motionless against her pack, with her back to the light. She doesn't look up when I approach but nods to my shadow. Virginia is down somewhere closer to the ice. Laura is looking at a crater of fine sand among the rocks below her, and in the pristine sand, at the antlers of a caribou, bleached ivory, still attached to a desiccated body silvered with wind drift. I descend into the pit, conscious of the shadows of my footprints, and try to break the rack for a piece in which to carve scrimshaw narratives tonight while the bannock cooks. The ivory crumbles green in my hand and shadows gape in the carcass as the sand shifts. I look up and Laura is watching; I climb from the disturbed scene to sit beside her. She says nothing.

What I admire most about Norman Elder and his quixotic search from the Amazon basin to the Sahara to the Canadian High Arctic for what he describes as the beautiful minds of people entirely at home with their place in the world is the recognition in his sometimes awkward writing of his own absurdity, his delight in the ironies of contemporary exploration, his terrified amusement at being only mortal in an unheroic age.

Oksitartok is inscribed in all sincerity by Lady Eaton with a wonderfully parodic echo of every foreword ever appended to an Arctic narrative:

> It pleases me to feel that Norman was inspired by my expedition to the Arctic to make this trip and write this book.

> I have a great respect for the Elder family. They are a very talented family, and have contributed much to the world of fox hunting in Canada.

Near the end of his book, Elder laconically acknowledges the yield of his experience in the dump near Resolute:

> Several hours photographing here gave
> Me enough material for a full
> Lecture series on our arctic heritage.

The Canadian soul may reside in the possibilities of natural chaos, the creative evasion of order revealed to us by Arctic landscape.

The Land of Feast and Famine shows a morbid fascination with the gossip of the north, especially images of death. But Helge Ingstad holds little sympathy for Hornby and others rumoured to have perished by starvation or violence; he seems determined to remain an observer, holding in derision the man who starved beside a stack of *Saturday Evening Posts*, the man who froze solid kneeling in front of a pile of kindling, matches clutched in his hand, or the man who shot his partner through the bottom of a top bunk, then wrote on bloodsplattered paper, I cant take no more, and killed himself where he lay — when they were found, the bunks had collapsed; they were so badly decomposed, their bodies had fused like compost and they were buried together along with their mouldering bedclothes. (Virginia and I camped on an open spit of gravel near where that happened, at the confluence of the Saline and the Mackenzie, July 24, 1989; in the middle of the night we heard a bear rummaging among the cabin ruins.)

Death and Deliverance: The Haunting True Story of the Hercules Crash at the North Pole. Polar Dream: The Heroic Saga of the First Solo Journey by a Woman and Her Dog to the Pole. Death and Deliverance in large print, Polar Dream in large print, titles proclaiming absolute north. The first, on the cover of a documentary account by Robert Mason Lee. The second, covering an adventure narrative by Helen Thayer. The Hercules crashed on Ellesmere, over 600 brutalizing kilometres from the pole. Thayer circumnavigated what her map identifies as "North Pole (Magnetic Centre)" during a twenty-seven-day ski trip off Bathurst Island; her travelling companion of the title, a black Canadian husky, was borrowed. Thayer is American. And in Canada, on Ellesmere, Hercules, the stumbling giant, falls; his true story, haunting: as if every story isn't true. And haunting.

This is from a prayer penned in 1871 by the Reverend Dr. Newman of Washington for an American expedition under the command of Charles Francis Hall, "to be used only on reaching the pole":

Great God of the universe!
We have seen Thy wonders upon the deep, and amidst the everlasting hills of ice, and now we behold the glory of Thy power in this place so long secluded from the gaze of civilized man. Unto Thee, who stretchest out the north over the empty place, and hangest the earth upon nothing; who hath compassed the waters with bounds until day and night come to an end; we give Thee thanks for what our eyes now behold, and for what our hearts now feel.
Bless the nation that sent us forth; bless the President of our great republic; bless all the people of our favored land, whose national banner we now wave over this distant country.

Max Buxton on April 11, 1988, Day 40 of the Canadian-Soviet Polar Bridge Expedition: We just got something on the radio from the bishop stating that "It would not be practical" to perform a wedding at the North Pole for the following reasons:

1) It was feared that the place would become more important than the event;
2) Geographically the Pole was not within the Christian community;
3) No premarital counselling had been conducted with the parties concerned.

Buxton's fiancée was to have flown to the pole. Laurie Dexter, an ordained expedition member (and running adversary of mine in two editions of the Midnight Sun Ultramarathon in Nanisivik), was to have performed the ceremony. So much for that.

The search for Ultima Thule is not itself ennobling, nor concomitant with visionary grace. The ordinary in extraordinary situations cannot animate collective desires, nor articulate communal dreams. Extremities of experience lead not only to Jerusalem or the pleasures of oblivion but, sometimes, most often now, to business contracts: Arctic adventurers with nothing to say cannot afford to say nothing.

I am writing the words of Ranulph Fiennes, of Robert Swan, of Will Steger, and of Richard Weber, each of whom has been to one or both poles a number of times in the past few years. I write their words and lose myself among them, in the moral emptiness, and cannot find myself within or even on the margins of their daunting narratives. Even Laurie Dexter, the man of God, seems less concerned in *Polar Bridge* with visions and with dreams than with keeping, on a ragged journey, visceral pride. And so, command/option all/delete.

Let us for a moment risk simplicity. We have read too many books perhaps and expect the visionary to be difficult, print positioning the ideal beyond our grasp. But imagine this: a book of poems, thoughtfully inscribed, retrieved from my mother-in-law's residual estate; a sketch, a pencilled countryside by Peggy Miller on page 25, complementing text by Brant Joseph Maracle. He is Tyendinaga Mohawk, and she Ojibwa. It is important to know this. The foreword is by Jay Silverheels, a Mohawk. The picture is of receding grassland, a few scrub trees, a shadowed sky through which hills break in the distance. In diminishing perspective there is an arrangement of carefully articulated blank spaces. The space in the middle distance is the size of a dime. It is the most precise, although like the others it is empty, detailed in outline only. A man in skin breeches sits on a grazing horse; the reins are loose in the man's off-side hand, his bare torso is turned slightly to the front, the two feathers in his hair catch the wind, a bow and quiver drape across his far shoulder, and his right arm, closest to the viewer, is raised in a gesture of acknowledgement. Miller's vision is simple. In the absence of people their presence fills the landscape.

Each of us, descendant of some passed-on traveller, has been paid for — each one, according to the words of Maya Angelou, speaking to America.
Survival is a political act for all but the survivor, bought by all the deaths preceding; I owe nothing but my life.

When Julia and Laura were in their early teens, we took them to the Sistine Chapel. It was a hot afternoon and the crowd was restless; the air overhead shimmered in a mild haze, softening Michelangelo's heroic images. I told them about Blake's etchings, and when we got to London, we saw his "Visions of the Daughters of Albion" in the British Museum, handling one of only several copies ever made, touching the paper Blake had coloured by hand. Between these two events we drove to Poland and visited Auschwitz. It was important to see this, too. In a blockhouse called *Canada*, I saw a suitcase among a pile of suitcases with the stencilled name, M. Cohen. Matt Cohen is a friend of mine. I lost all thought in the overpowering rush of feeling; time reeled, and the vertigo of unsecured imagination clenched my soul. I thought that I was dead. There was only past. Outside and in again; then somewhere else. Julia called me quietly to see a tiny cell in Block Eleven, but I reached out my hand to her in the dark corridor and we walked away into the slanted light. With Laura and Virginia we moved along a cobbled road to a low red brick building surrounded by lush grass, where Anne Frank had been kept with her mother and sister before being shipped to Bergen-Belsen. Later we visited her room in Amsterdam within earshot of St. Mary's-something-Church.

Between history as requiem and history as celebration falls the shadow of the present. I didn't say this first, but it's important to say it now: history is no longer possible.

In the Eglise de Bonne Espérance at Fort Good Hope on the Mackenzie, half a day's paddle from the Arctic Circle, every surface of the small interior is painted in a variety of patterns and designs. Visionary murals, portraits, and devotional tableaux in caribou blood, ash, and floral emulsions contend for the sifting light through coloured glass. The air is thick with the effluvium of dry rot and disinfectant, the oily smell of shellac and candle wax and kerosene. Three days to the north, a thousand kilometres from Fort Simpson where we started, we come upon a derelict cabin and some crumbling outbuildings, what is left of Barney Fischer's Trading Post. I am sad the people are gone and sad with the pastness of things, but Virginia notes her pleasure, the duration of their happiness apparent in the hand-hewn floorboards, the carved end of a wigwam pole, nails from hand-forged to ardox, the turf growing on the skewed roof, rich with flowers.

Jim Green, writing from his tent at Angoyaktoovik in the early 1970s:

> the lake looks all pale
> moving just a little
> by shifting night airs
> between cold black rocks
>
> the far shore is dark
> horizon   lighter
> with a streak of pink
> the only sign of colour
> in a dozen shades of grey

Sometimes it is as simple as that. The world implies our presence by the light perceived.

On the Arctic ice in May, I am its text, impressionable, inscribable (invisibled by awe). Aritha van Herk writes this, fragile as any silenced voice, a tracement of Arctic essence. She is riding in a komatik, slamming over frozen broken water, wrapped in caribou against bruises and the cold, thinking the words of another language, Pijamini's Inuktitut nouns which, in their rehearsal, she dreams will set her free.

Superman flies deep into the Arctic ice to commune with a holograph of Jor-El, his natural father, who is dead. The North Pole: it's just a thing you discover, says Christopher Robin carelessly, not being quite sure himself. The Waterloo County of Homer Watson belonged to Constable; the floodwater flats of the Grand River Valley held brief pools in the spring to spear carp, if you were lucky; the dreams of Mennonites and Mohawks, Germans and Ontario Scotch coalesced where the Speed meets the Grand, in English blood; my ancestry is Canadian. My childhood won't fit easily into words. My parents' past erased my present, as a child. I need to say this before it's too late. My relationship with my father and mother, who are dead now, is still volatile, although we are mutually more tolerant. I remember their lives from before I was born. The past, rhapsodic — George and Mary — always thrilling, anecdotal, green or golden, made most of my experience growing up seem incidental, a fluttering of stilted photographs. There was no malice; but mine was a colonial childhood. It was necessary to invent myself from black and white — this is the closest I will ever come to confession — a creation of consciousness, a creature of language. Like Canada, I am slow to become who I am; although finally, within the landscape of my own particular Arctic, I become myself.

Get inside the whale — admit you are inside (for you *are*, of course). Accept it, endure it, record it. This is Eric Blair's admonition to the writer of his time, my parents' time. Be an unconstructive Jonah, Whitman among the corpses, at least until the world has shaken itself into its new shape. The world will change, but the writer as writer changes nothing (he said). The swallower swallowed, the writer at best is proof that we endure. Yet he altered us; as George Orwell he moulded private visions into public prophecy, made metaphysics political. He turned the whale into an ocean.

These words here now refuse to cast my life as prelude. I have been waiting to write this for a long time, and now I find in words the silence I have dreamed of dreaming. In silence I have found the words to speak. Not only is my story a story to be shared, this landscape the language of our secret aspirations and our common terrors, but the past that I inherit is mine to leave, to shape, to free the future from obsessions with itself. My politics are metaphysical; the Arctic I articulate, envision personal, a public legacy.

Rudy Wiebe in *Playing Dead* and Penny Petrone in *Northern Voices* share with their readers the song of the Igloolik shaman Uvavnuk. Her words were recorded in translation by both Knud Rasmussen and Peter Freuchen:

The great sea	The great sea moves me!
Has set me adrift:	The great sea sets me adrift!
It moves me as a small plant	It moves me like algae on stones
in the running river,	In running brook water.
Earth and the mighty weather	The vault of heaven
Move Me,	Moves me!
Storm through me,	The mighty weather storms
Have carried me away,	Through my soul. It tears me
	with it.
And I tremble with joy.	I tremble with joy.

In *Playing Dead* Wiebe explores the Arctic in a metaphysical adventure that, on the surface, seems skillful navigation through an archipelago of random thoughts, quotations, observations, exhortations, mediations, meditations, documentary excerpts, judgements, visions, memories, and dreams. Some of the writing is very powerful and, everywhere, is passionate. Nothing he encounters in the Arctic is an obstacle, although much he finds a challenge. If there is horror, he marks the grave. If there is beauty, he sings its praise. But what makes this work especially inspired is the humility of its vision in which everything converges as the writer's spirit bonds with the Arctic landscape of his own imagining.

Skiing the frozen shoreline of southern Greenland in the winter of 1993, I look from Europe to America. My hosts speak among themselves in a dialect of Inuktitut, shifting easily to Danish and shyly to English. Several are polar Inuit, and one is descended from survivors of the Qitdlarssuaq migration from Baffin in the 1860s. I am too much aware of Canada as an Arctic nation to think of the Arctic in my own experience as an expression of privilege, the Arctic of Canada as residue of the Imperial enterprise, or Ultima Thule as a colonial project, and skiing in brilliant sunshine that catches spring snow sliding off the skis into eddies of whirling light, I research my thoughts for the historical moment when geography and history merged in the Canadian imagination.

The vocabulary of postcolonial critical theory creates the illusion I can think this through: enterprise, project, moment — as if the past were intentional, a schematic construct. Against my own mixed blood, in the resonance of our languages and dialects, in the exploding parallels behind us on the snow and the great gap of open, ice-strewn water of the Davis Strait before us, theory itself is an expression of privilege — reduction of the past to abstraction, of heritage to evasions of natural chaos.

Where I live, writes Ursula K. LeGuin, is to men a wilderness. But to me it is home. This I found in a book called *Healing the Wounds: The Promise of Ecofeminism*. The editor, Judith Plant, grieves in celebration of convergent lives.

I will persist with the word wilderness
over silence
but it has become
in worlds superimposed on one another
our common ground
of difference.

Wolves of the night air move through us; our familiarity with bears as brute shadows of the human form is a Canadian obsession; we make love with bears, with seals; and whales pass easily over and around us. Sometimes we become the bear; sometimes the bear, the seal, the whale is us. Julia Moss describes, in "North from the Metro Zoo," being swallowed by the polar bear she rescued, after having draped herself around it to become a bear in woman's clothing:

> I'll crave blubber
> crunch seal bones
>
> our seal and saltwater breath
> will carve snow chambers
> in our house
> will be many mansions

How far north will a mind consent? J. Michael Yates in *The Great Bear Lake Meditations:*

> There were some secrets I wished to conceal from the wilderness, but a wind detected whiskey on my breath. . . .

Rumbling among present participles, between stasis and process, thundering above the slurred tidewaters of Tassiajjuaq and over frozen Soper Falls, riding the tumultuous ice along the Kuujuaq, the river hollowed between risen permafrost and crystal sky — kill engines, smoke (not me), drink tea made from ice carried with us, meltwater fresh from aeons at rest. You think I'm going to talk about literature. I am going to talk about literature. Look for me among words. When I am no longer alive, look here. Between river and shore, stones and the ocean, in echoes of a poem by Pablo Neruda rounding the devotional rhetoric of Rudy Wiebe. Look here, among words. Swirling Arctic snow sweeps over unseen promontories, eddies in the lee of phantom contours, streams peculiar parallels across the tundra. In winter you can see the wind; the river is an absence, shape of the land's memory, while flowers in their causes sleep. Look for me here, in the silencing of words; look here, I am tremulous with language, between wind and the land.

And so ends this day.

BIBLIOGRAPHY

*N*OTHING WRITTEN is by accident, nor is it always by design: the following are books and articles cited in the pages preceding. Many works not listed were of equal value but to include them here would be impossible, since each text leads to such a variety of others and every copy of a text is different, in the reading if not as artifact — so that all the libraries of the world could not hold their multiplicity.

Abramson, Howard S. *Hero in Disgrace: The True Discoverer of the North Pole, Frederick A. Cook.* New York: Paragon House, 1991.

Alexander, Bryan, and Cherry Alexander. *The Inuit: Hunters of the North.* Text and Photographs. Godalming: Bramley, 1988.

Amundsen, Roald. *My Life as an Explorer.* New York: Doubleday, Page, 1927.

_____. *The North West Passage.* London: Constable, 1908.

Atwood, Margaret. *Wilderness Tips.* Toronto: McClelland and Stewart, 1991.

_____. "Concerning Franklin and His Gallant Crew" ("A condensed version of one of Atwood's 1991 Clarendon Lectures at Oxford University, delivered 18th April of this year."). *Books in Canada* (May 1991).

Back, Captain George, *Narrative of the Arctic Land Expedition to the Mouth of the Great Fish River, and along the Shores of the Arctic Ocean in the Years 1833, 1834, and 1835.* London: Murray, 1836.

Beattie, Owen, and John Geiger. *Frozen in Time: Unlocking the Secrets of the Franklin Expedition.* Saskatoon: Western Prairie Producer, 1988.

Beedell, Mike. See Edward Struzik, below; and Jeff MacInnis, below (credit for participation largely obscured).

Berton, Pierre. *The Arctic Grail: The Quest for the North West Passage and the North Pole, 1819–1909.* Toronto: McClelland and Stewart, 1988.

Blake, E. Vale, ed. *Arctic Experiences; Containing Capt. George E. Tyson's Wonderful Drift on the Ice-Floe, A History of the Polaris Expedition, The Cruise of the Tigress, and Rescue of the Polaris Survivors, To Which Is Added a General Arctic Chronology.* New York: Harper and Brothers, 1874.

Bockstoce, John. *Arctic Passages.* New York: Hearst Marine Books, 1991.

Bowering, George. "More Like Mark Trail." *Another Mouth.* Toronto: McClelland and Stewart, 1979.

Breummer, Fred. *Arctic World,* principal writer and photographer. Toronto: Key Porter, 1985.

_____. *World of the Polar Bear.* Toronto: Key Porter, 1989.

_____. *Arctic Memories: Living with the Inuit.* Toronto: Key Porter, 1993.

Brody, Hugh. *The People's Land: Eskimos and Whites in the Eastern Arctic.* Harmondsworth, Eng.: Penguin, 1975.

_____. *Maps and Dreams.* Vancouver: Douglas and McIntyre, 1981.

_____. *Living Arctic: Hunters of the Canadian North.* Vancouver: Douglas and McIntyre, 1987.

Browne, James A. *The North-West Passage and the Fate of Sir John Franklin.* Woolwich, Eng.: W. P. Jackson, 1860.

Burt, Page. *Barrenland Beauties: Showy Plants of the Arctic Coast.* Yellowknife, NWT: Outcrop, 1991.

Canadian Heritage Rivers System: Nomination Document for the Soper River. No place of publication given, 1991.

Cartwright, George. *A Journal of Transactions and Events During a Residence of Nearly Sixteen Years on the Coast of Labrador Containing Many Interesting Particulars, Both of the Country and Its Inhabitants, Not Hitherto Known.* Newark, NJ: Allin and Ridge, 1792.

Christian, Edgar. *Unflinching: A Diary of Tragic Adventure.* London: John Murray, 1937. See also Whalley, George, ed. *Death in the Barren Ground: Edgar Christian.* Ottawa: Oberon, 1980. Identified on clothbound spine as *The Diary of Edgar Christian.*

Christopher, Robert. "Narrators of the Arctic: Images and Movements in Northland Narratives." *The American Review of Canadian Studies* 18.3 (1988).

Chung, In-Cho. *Eastern North America as Seen by a Botanist: Pictorial (1. The Arctic Region).* Daytona Beach, FL: self-published, 1989.

Cook, Frederick. *My Attainment of the Pole.* New York: Polar, 1911.

Crnkovich, Mary, ed. "Gossip." *A Spoken History of Women of the North.* Ottawa: Canadian Arctic Resources Committee, 1990.

Davidson, John West, and John Rugge. *Great Heart: The History of a Labrador Adventure.* New York: Penguin, 1988.

de Cuchilleros, Jorge. *The Invention of Time.* Trans. Luis E. Melendez. Madrid: Prado Editores, 1984.

de Poncins, Gontran. *Kabloona.* In collaboration with Lewis Galantiere. Virginia: Time-Life Books, 1965. Reprinted 1980. Original edition, Reynal, 1941.

Diubaldo, Richard J. *Stefansson and the Canadian Arctic.* Montreal: McGill-Queen's UP, 1978.

Douglas, George M. *Lands Forlorn: The Story of an Expedition to Hearne's Coppermine River.* New York: Putnam's, 1914.

Drummond, Robbie Newton. *Arctic Circle Songs*. Waterloo: Penumbra, 1991.

Duden, Barbara. *The Woman Beneath the Skin*. Trans. Thomas Dunlap. Cambridge, MA: Harvard UP, 1992.

Eber, Dorothy Harley. *When the Whalers Were Up North: Inuit Memories of the Eastern Arctic*. Kingston: McGill-Queen's UP, 1989.

Elder, Norman. *Oksitartok*. Toronto: self-published, 1967.

Fagan, Brian M. *The Great Journey: The Peopling of Ancient America*. New York: Thames and Hudson, 1987.

Flaherty, Robert J. *My Eskimo Friends: "Nanook of the North."* New York: Doubleday, Page, 1924.

Forster, E. M. *Howards End*. New York: Bantam, 1985.

Franklin, Captain John. *Narrative of a Journey to the Shores of the Polar Sea*. Edmonton: Hurtig, 1969.

_____. *Narrative of a Second Expedition to the Shores of the Polar Sea in the Years 1825, 1826, and 1827*. London: Murray, 1828. Edmonton: Hurtig, 1971.

Freuchen, Peter. *Book of the Eskimos*. Cleveland: World Publishing, 1961.

Geddes, Gary, ed. *15 Canadian Poets x 2*. Toronto: Oxford, 1988.

Glover, Richard, ed. *A Journey to the Northern Ocean (A Journey from Prince of Wales's Fort in Hudson's Bay to the Northern Ocean, 1769, 1770, 1771, 1772)* by Samuel Hearne. Toronto: Macmillan, 1958. See also Samuel Hearne; Farley Mowat; J. B. Tyrrell.

Green, Jim. *North Book*. Burnaby, BC: Blackfish, 1975.

Gunnars, Kristjana. *The Prowler*. Red Deer, AB: Red Deer College Press, 1989.

Hall, Captain Charles Francis. *Life with the Esquimaux; A Narrative of Arctic Experience in Search of Survivors of Sir John Franklin's Expedition*. London: Sampson, Low, 1865.

Hamelin, Louis-Edmond. *Canadian Nordicity: It's Your North, Too.* Trans. William Barr. Montreal: Harvest House, 1979.

Hanbury, David T. *A Journey from Chesterfield Inlet to Great Slave Lake, 1898–99.* N.p.: n.p., [1900?].

_____. *Sport and Travel in the Northland of Canada.* London: Edward Arnold, 1904.

Harper, Kenn. *Give Me My Father's Body: The Life of Minik, The New York Eskimo.* Newmarket, ON: Blacklead, 1986.

Hawking, Stephen. *A Brief History of Time: From the Big Bang to Black Holes.* New York: Bantam, 1990.

Hearne, Samuel. *A Journey from Prince of Wales's Fort, in Hudson's Bay to the Northern Ocean in the Years 1769, 1770, 1771, 1772.* London: Strahan and Cadell, 1795. See also Richard Glover; Farley Mowat; J. B. Tyrrell.

Heilbrun, Carolyn G. *Writing a Woman's Life.* New York: Ballantine, 1989.

Honderich, John. *Arctic Imperative: Is Canada Losing the North?* Toronto: University of Toronto Press, 1987.

Horwood, Harold. *Bartlett: The Great Canadian Explorer.* Toronto: Doubleday, 1977.

Howe, Joseph. "Acadia." *Nineteenth-Century Narrative Poems.* Ed. David Sinclair. Toronto: McClelland and Stewart, 1972.

Hubbard, Mina. *A Woman's Way Through Unknown Labrador.* London: John Murray, 1908.

Hunt, William K. *Stef: A Biography of Vilhjalmur Stefansson, Canadian Arctic Explorer.* Vancouver: University of British Columbia Press, 1986.

Ingstad, Helge. *The Land of Feast and Famine.* Trans. Eugene Gay-Tifft. Montreal: McGill-Queen's UP, 1992. *Pelsjergerliv Blandt Nord-Kanadas Indiianere.* Oslo: Glydendal Norsk Forlag, 1931.

Jenness, Diamond. *The People of the Twilight.* Chicago: University of Chicago Press, 1975. Macmillan, 1928.

Kane, Elisha Kent. *The United States Grinnell Expedition in Search of Sir John Franklin; A Personal Narrative.* New York: Sheldon, Blakeman, 1857.

_____. *Arctic Explorations in the Years 1853, '54, '55.* Philadelphia: Childs and Peterson, 1856.

Kelly, M. T. "Land Before Time." *Saturday Night* 104.7 (July 1989).

Kenyon, Walter. *Arctic Argonauts.* Ed. M. T. Kelly. Waterloo: Penumbra, 1990. See also Jens Munk.

Karasick, Adeena. *The Empress Has No Closure.* Vancouver: Talonbooks, 1992.

Kroetsch, Robert. *Completed Field Notes.* Toronto: McClelland and Stewart, 1989.

Lavin-Moss, Virginia. "The Imagined Arctic: A Northern Reader." Manuscript. See John Moss, below.

Lee, Robert Mason. *Death and Deliverance: The Haunting True Story of the Hercules Crash at the North Pole.* Toronto: Macfarlane Walter and Ross, 1992.

London, Jack. *Works of Jack London.* New York: Avenel, 1980.

Lopez, Barry. *Arctic Dreams: Imagination and Desire in a Northern Landscape.* Toronto: Bantam, 1987. Scribner's 1986.

Low, A. P. *Cruise of the* Neptune: *Report on the Dominion Government Expedition to Hudson Bay and the Arctic Islands on Board the DGS Neptune 1903–04.* Ottawa: Government Printing Bureau, 1906.

Lowe, Ronald. *Kangiryuarmiut Uqauhingita Numiktittitdjutingit.* Inuvik: Committee for Original Peoples Entitlement, 1983.

Lyall, Ernie. *An Arctic Man.* Edmonton: Hurtig, 1979.

Mackenzie, Alexander. *Voyages from Montreal on the River St. Laurence Through the Continent of North America to the Frozen and Pacific Oceans in the Years 1789 and 1793*. London: Cadell, 1801. Edmonton: Hurtig, 1971.

MacInnis, Jeff, and Wade Rowlands. *Polar Passage: The Historic First Sail Through the Northwest Passage*. Toronto: Random House, 1989.

MacLennan, Hugh. *Scotchman's Return, and Other Essays*. Toronto: Macmillan, 1960.

Maracle, Brant Joseph. *The Fever and Frustration of the Indian Heart*. Oshawa, ON: Maracle Press, 1972.

Markham, Captain A. H. *The Great Frozen Sea. A Personal Narrative of the Voyage of the* Alert *During the Arctic Expedition of 1875/6*. London: Daldy, Isbister, 1878.

Marlatt, Daphne. *Ana Historic*. Toronto: Coach House Press, 1988.

Mary-Rousselière, Guy. *Qitdlarssuaq: The Story of a Polar Migration*. Trans. Alan Cooke. Winnipeg: Wuerz, 1991. *Qitdlarssuaq: l'histoire d'une migration polaire*. Montreal: Les Presses de l'Université de Montréal, 1980.

Maxwell, Moreau S. *Archaeology of the Lake Harbour District, Baffin Island*. Ottawa: National Museums of Canada, 1973.

M'Clintock, Captain F. L. *A Narrative of the Fate of Sir John Franklin and His Companions. The Voyage of the* Fox *in the Arctic Seas*. London: John Murray, 1859.

M'Clure, R. L. *The Discovery of the North-West Passage by HMS* Investigator *1850–54*. Ed. Sherard Osborn. Edmonton: Hurtig, 1969.

McGhee, Robert. *Beluga Hunters: An Archaeological Reconstruction of the History and Culture of the Mackenzie Delta Kittegaryumiut*. Hull, PQ: Canadian Museum of Civilization, 1988. Memorial University: 1974.

_____. *Canadian Arctic Prehistory.* Toronto: Van Nostrand Reinhold, 1978.

McGuffin, Gary, and Joanie McGuffin. *Where Rivers Run.* Toronto: Stoddart, 1988.

McMahon, Kevin. *Arctic Twilight.* Toronto: Lorimer, 1988.

Mear, Roger, and Robert Swan. *A Walk to the Pole: To the Heart of Antarctica in the Footsteps of Scott.* New York: Crown, 1987.

Miertsching, Johann August. *Frozen Ships: The Arctic Diary of Johann Miertsching, 1850–1854.* Trans., with intro. and notes, L. H. Neatby. New York: St. Martin's Press, 1967.

Minh-ha, Trin T. *Woman, Native, Other.* Bloomington, IN: Indiana UP, 1989.

Moss, Edward L. *Shores of the Polar Sea.* A Narrative of the Arctic Expedition of 1875–6. London: M. Ward , 1878.

Moss, John. "Imagining the Arctic," *Arctic Circle* 1.5 (March/April 1991).

_____. *Arctic Landscape and the Metaphysics of Geography.* London: Canadian High Commission, 1991.

_____, and Virginia Lavin-Moss. "The Imagined Arctic: A Northern Reader." Manuscript.

Moss, Julia. "North from the Metro Zoo." Unpublished.

Mowat, Farley. *Coppermine Journey: An Account of a Great Adventure Selected from the Journals of Samuel Hearne.* Toronto: McClelland and Stewart, 1958. See also Richard Glover; Samuel Hearne; J. B. Tyrrell.

_____. *The Desperate People.* Toronto: McClelland and Stewart, 1959.

_____. *The People of the Deer.* Toronto: McClelland and Stewart, 1975.

_____. *The Snow Walker.* Toronto: McClelland and Stewart, 1975.

Munk, Jens. *The Journal of Jens Munk: 1619–1620.* Ed. W. A. Kenyon, from the translation by C. C. A. Gosch, vol. 97 of the Hakluyt Society, 1897. Toronto: Royal Ontario Museum, 1980.

Nansen, Fridtjof. *Farthest North.* London: Macmillan's Colonial Library, 1897.

Nares, Sir George Strong. *Narrative of a Voyage to the Polar Sea During 1875–6 in HM Ships* Alert *and* Discovery; *with Notes on the Natural History by H. W. Fielden.* London: Low, Marston, Searle, and Rivington, 1878.

Neatby, L. H. See Johann Miertsching.

_____. *In Quest of the Northwest Passage.* Toronto: Longmans, Green, 1958.

_____. *Conquest of the Last Frontier.* Don Mills, ON: Longmans, 1966.

Nuyviak, Felix. "A Long Time Ago/Memories." Recorded and translated by Nellie Cournoyea. Manuscript at Inuvaluit Regional Corp., Inuvik, NWT.

Ondaatje, Michael. *In the Skin of a Lion.* Markham, ON: Penguin, 1988.

Onley, Toni. *Onley's Arctic: Diaries and Paintings of the High Arctic.* Vancouver: Douglas and McIntyre, 1989.

Orwell, George. "Inside the Whale." In *Selected Essays.* Harmondsworth, Eng.: Penguin, 1960.

Peary, Robert. *Nearest the Pole: A Narrative of the Polar Expedition of the Peary Arctic Club.* London: Hutchinson, 1907.

_____. *The North Pole: Its Discovery Under the Auspices of the Peary Arctic Club.* Toronto: Copp, Clark, 1910.

Perkins, Robert. *Into the Great Solitude: An Arctic Journey.* New York: Henry Holt, 1991.

Petrone, Penny, ed. *Northern Voices: Inuit Writing in English*. Toronto: University of Toronto Press, 1988.

Pike, Warburton. *The Barren Ground of Northern Canada*. London: Macmillan, 1892.

Plant, Judith. *Healing the Wounds: The Promise of Ecofeminism*. Toronto: Between the Lines, 1990.

Porteous, J. D. *Landscapes of the Mind: Worlds of Sense and Metaphor.* Toronto: University of Toronto Press, 1990.

Pryde, Duncan. *Nunaga: Ten Years of Eskimo Life*. New York: Walker, 1971.

Purdy, Al. *The Collected Poems of Al Purdy*. Edited by Russell Brown. Toronto: McClelland and Stewart, 1986.

Raffan, James. *Summer North of Sixty: By Paddle and Portage Across the Barren Lands*. Toronto: Key Porter, 1990.

_____. "Frontier, Homeland, and Sacred Place." Ph.D. dissertation, Department of Geography, Queen's University, Kingston. Unpublished, 1992.

_____. "Where God Began." *Equinox* 71 (October 1993).

Rasmussen, Knud. *Across Arctic America: Narrative of the Fifth Thule Expedition from Melville Bay to Cape Morris Jessup*. London: Putnam's, 1927.

Richardson, John. *Arctic Ordeal: The Journal of John Richardson, Surgeon-Naturalist with Franklin, 1820–1822*. Edited by C. Stuart Houston. Montreal: McGill-Queen's UP, 1984.

Ruggles, Richard I. *A Country So Interesting: The Hudson's Bay Company and Two Centuries of Mapping, 1670–1870*. Montreal: McGill-Queen's UP, 1991.

Scott, F. R. *The Collected Poems of F. R. Scott*. Toronto: McClelland and Stewart, 1981.

Service, Robert. *Collected Poems of Robert Service*. New York: Dodd, Mead, 1940.

Shek, Ben-Z. "Yves Thériault: The Would-be Amerindian and His Imaginary Inuit." *The Canadian North: Essays in Culture and Literature*. Eds. Jorn Carleson and Bengt Streijffert. Lund: Nordic Association for Canadian Studies, 1989.

Shelley, Mary Wollstonecraft. *Frankenstein; or, The Modern Prometheus*. New York: Pocket Books, 1976. Ed. James Reiger, variant readings from the 1818 and 1831 editions.

Shurke, Paul. See Will Steger.

Soper, J. Dewey. *Canadian Arctic Recollections Baffin Island 1923–31*. Saskatoon: Institute for Northern Studies, 1981.

Spalding, Alex. *Learning to Speak Inuktitut. A Grammar of North Baffin Dialects*. London, ON: Centre for Research and Teaching of Canadian Native Languages, University of Western Ontario, 1979.

Stefansson, Vilhjalmur. *The Friendly Arctic: The Story of Five Years in the Polar Regions*. New York. Macmillan, 1921.

_____. *My Life with the Eskimo*. New York: Collier Books, 1966.

Steffler, John. *The Afterlife of George Cartwright*. Toronto: McClelland and Stewart, 1992.

Steger, Will, with Paul Shurke. *North to the Pole*. New York: Ballantine, 1987.

Struzik, Edward, Photography by Mike Beedell. *Northwest Passage: The Quest for an Arctic Route to the East*. Toronto: Key Porter, 1991.

Swan, Robert. *Icewalk*. London: Jonathan Cape, 1990. See also Roger Mear.

Thayer, Helen. *Polar Dream: The Heroic Saga of the First Solo Journey by a Woman and Her Dog to the Pole*. New York: Simon and Shuster, 1993.

Thériault, Yves. *Agaguk.* Trans. Miriam Chapin. Toronto: McGraw-Hill Ryerson, 1967.

Thibert, Arthur. *Dictionary Eskimo-English English Eskimo.* Ottawa: Canadian Research Centre for Anthropology, Saint Paul University, 1970.

Thomas, Audrey. "The More Little Mummy in the World." *Ladies and Escorts.* Ottawa: Oberon, 1977.

Tuttle, Charles R. *Our North Land: Being a Full Account of the Canadian North-West and Hudson's Bay Route, Together with a Narrative of the Experiences of the Hudson's Bay Expedition of 1884, Including a Description of the Climate, Resources, and the Characteristics of the Native Inhabitants Between the 50th Parallel and the Arctic Circle.* Toronto: Blackett Robinson, 1885.

Tyrrell, J. B., ed. *A Journey from Prince of Wales's Fort, in Hudson's Bay to the Northern Ocean in the Years 1769, 1770, 1771, 1772.* By Samuel Hearne. Toronto: The Champlain Society, 1911. See also Richard Glover; Samuel Hearne; Farley Mowat.

_____. *Across the Sub-Arctics of Canada.* Toronto: William Briggs, 1908.

Tyson, George E. *Tyson's Arctic Experiences.* See entry under E. Vale Blake, above.

van Herk, Aritha. *Places Far from Ellesmere.* Red Deer: Red Deer College Press, 1990.

_____. *In Visible Ink: Crypto-Frictions.* Edmonton: NeWest, 1991.

Verne, Jules. *Adventures of Captain Hatteras: The English at the North Pole.* Vol. 2, *Works of Jules Verne.* Edited by Charles F. Horne. New York: Vincent Parke, 1911. Translator not given. Originally published in 1865.

Waldron, Malcolm. *Snow Man.* Boston: Houghton Mifflin, 1931.

Wallace, Dillon. *The Lure of the Labrador Wild.* St. John's, NF: Breakwater, 1983. Revell, 1905.

Weber, Richard, and Laurie Dexter, Christopher Holloway, Max Buxton. *Polar Bridge*. Toronto: Key Porter, 1990.

Weems, John Edward. *Race for the Pole*. New York: Holt, 1960.

_____. *Peary: The Explorer and the Man*. Los Angeles: Tarcher, 1967.

Whalley, George. *The Legend of John Hornby*. London: John Murray, 1962.

Whalley, George. Ed. *Death in the Barren Ground: Edgar Christian*. Ottawa: Oberon Press, 1980. Identified on clothbound spine as *The Diary of Edgar Christian*.

Wiebe, Rudy. *Where Is the Voice Coming From?* Toronto: McClelland and Stewart, 1974.

_____. *Playing Dead. A Contemplation Concerning the Arctic*. Edmonton: NeWest, 1989.

Wilkinson, Douglas. *Land of the Long Day*. Toronto: Clarke, Irwin, 1955.

Woodman, David C. *Unravelling the Franklin Mystery: Inuit Testimony*. Montreal: McGill-Queen's UP, 1991.

Yates, J. Michael. *The Completely Collapsible Portable Man*. Oakville, ON: Mosaic, 1984.

Young, Oran. R. *Arctic Politics: Conflict and Cooperation in the Circumpolar North*. Dartmouth College: University Press of New England, 1992.

ACKNOWLEDGEMENTS

I WOULD LIKE to express my appreciation for aid in preparing this project to Graham Farquarson, president of Strathcona Mines in Nanisivik, Baffin Island, to Joe Womersley who, together with Graham, Fred and Karen Bailey, and Linda Brunner, makes running with the midnight sun a possibility; to Michael Hellyer at the Canadian High Commission in London for his support and encouragement; to Roy Vontobel, founding editor of *Arctic Circle*, for his indulgence; also to the University of Ottawa, for its indulgence; to First Air for returning the ski pole and donating freight charges for books to Baffin, to Canadian Airlines, and to the amazing women and men who pilot Twin Otters throughout the Arctic, for getting us there; to Harvest Foodworks for keeping us well-fed where country food is unavailable; to the many people of the Arctic who have shown us hospitality beyond all expectation; to the Kooneeliusie family of Broughton Island and Joave Alavuktuk of Pangnirtung; to Pauloosie Kooneeliusie and his friend Jacobee for an exhilarating and exhausting thirty hours on the ice and for the quiet times while we waited for the wind to drop, on the way to North Pang Fiord; to Les and Brenda Bancroft with the RCMP at Fort Norman on the Deh Cho; to Frank and Adeline for sharing their camp upriver from Fort Good Hope; and to our friends Michael and Alice Barton in Inuvik, Steen Rasmussen and his family in Nuuk, Kerry Duncan in Iqaluit, and Geri Bailey in Pang; to David Monteith in Iqaluit for his generosity and invaluable assistance while we've been travelling Nunavut; to Jim Bell, the present editor of *Arctic Circle*, Denise Bekkama of the Nunatta Sunaqutangit Museum, Rick Hamburg at Economic Development and Tourism, and Elizabeth McIsaac for sharing her research and eager interest; to my good friend Graeme Dargo in Lake Harbour, and to Pam and the boys, to the Avavak family in Lake Harbour, especially Sandy and Anneak, Jawlie and Naomi, Moosa and Pitseoluk, to Matthew and Pingoatuk, Dale and Jo, Tom — in fact, to the whole Baffin community of Lake Harbour which, of all the embracing places in the Arctic I have been, feels most like home; to Bernd Dietz in the Canary Islands for his prescience; to Jake Dougherty, David Helwig, Hugh Hood, Daphne Marlatt, Ian Underhill, Matt Cohen, Carol Martin, Robert Kroetsch, and Linda Hutcheon, whose names mentioned here in deep appreciation for their encouragement does not mean they cannot distance themselves critically from the text they saw in earlier forms; to Maurice Cutler for the image of Scott's frozen corpse at sea; to my brother Richard for sharing his ingenuous enthusiasms; to Bruce and Carol Hodgins, John Wadland and the whole Wanapitei experience; to the audiences in Temagami, Nanisivik, Iqaluit, Oslo, London, Nuuk, Tenerife, Guelph, Montreal, Ottawa, and elsewhere, whose ways of listening helped to shape the final manuscript; to Charis Wahl for polishing that manuscript without undue abrasives; to Michael Carroll for his careful reading and the final touches; to Julia and George, Laura and Fred, to whom this book is dedicated; and, most of all, to Virginia for being there even when it hasn't made a lot of sense. Some parts of *Enduring Dreams* were published in different versions in *Arctic Circle, Canadian Fiction Magazine, The Canadian Forum, Ultramarathon Canada*, and the *Journal of Canadian Studies*, as well as in a monograph entitled *Arctic Landscape and the Metaphysics of Geography*, Canada House Lecture Series Number 51, published by the Canadian High Commission, London, England, in 1991. Fragments of this book were published under other authorship, by writers to whom I literally owe more than I can say. Writing under the broad rubric of literary criticism, I have quoted various texts without express permission. Under the aegis of creativity I have treated everything already written as a landscape in which imagination might explore with relative impugnity. It has not been my intention to diminish the work of others by turning their words to my own end. The Arctic will endure us all.